How to . . .

get the most from your
COLES NOTES

Key Point

Basic concepts in point form.

Close Up

Additional hints, notes, tips or background information.

Watch Out!

Areas where problems frequently occur.

Quick Tip

Concise ideas to help you learn what you need to know.

Remember This!

Essential material for mastery of the topic.

How to get an *A* in . . .

Senior
Algebra

Non-linear equations

Exponential functions

Logarithmic functions

© Copyright 1998 and Published by
COLES PUBLISHING. A division of Prospero Books
Toronto – Canada
Printed in Canada

Cataloguing in Publication Data
Price, David, 1952–

How to get an A in—senior algebra

(Coles notes)   ISBN 0-7740-0558-0

1. Algebra - Problems, exercises, etc.
2. Logarithms - Problems, exercises, etc.
3. Exponents (Algebra) - Problems, exercises, etc.
I. Title. II. Series

QA154.2.P74 1998   512'.0076   C98-931526-6

Publisher: Nigel Berrisford
Editing: Paul Kropp Communications
Book design and layout: Karen Petherick

Manufactured by Webcom Limited
Cover finish: Webcom's Exclusive DURACOAT

Contents

Introduction

Many students find algebra among the most difficult subjects in their school careers, probably because algebra is the study of the abstract. Unlike math subjects taken earlier in school such as arithmetic and geometry, algebra deals with numbers and concepts in an abstract state. This is why it seems removed from real life and is sometimes difficult to visualize. But this doesn't mean that algebra isn't useful. Every invention ever made, every building ever designed, every work of art ever painted started with an abstract plan. Algebra is how this is done in mathematics.

Universities consider proficiency in algebra as a good predictor for success in the sciences and engineering. Why? Because algebra teaches a discipline: if one learns the rules and follows the steps, the answers will come. Algebra may never be easy, but how successful you will be in handling it really depends on the effort you are willing to put in.

Exponents were invented to express large numbers in a convenient way. Such numbers are important in many fields, such as astronomy, physics, chemistry and medicine. Logarithms are just exponents in reverse. The use of logarithms led to the invention of the calculator. Today logarithms are still used in a wide variety of applications – compound interest, population growth, sound intensity, earthquake intensity and star brightness calculations.

Senior algebra, exponents and logarithms are important pre-calculus skills. Mastery of the discipline of senior algebra will give you important tools for tackling many subjects in university and beyond.

Other Coles Notes covering topics in senior mathematics:

Topics in senior math are frequently interconnected at each grade level. These additional titles from Coles Notes will help you master them all:

How to Get an A in ...

- Trigonometry and Circle Geometry
- Sequences and Series
- Permutations, Combinations & Probability
- Statistics and Data Analysis
- Calculus

Factoring

To factor an expression is to find two or more expressions which, when multiplied together, give the original expression.

FACTORING TRINOMIALS

Factoring trinomials is one of the most common procedures in algebra. The procedure is simple:

How to factor trinomials of the form $x^2 + bx + c$

To factor $x^2 + bx + c$, first find two numbers 'm' and 'n' which add to 'b' and at the same time multiply to 'c'. The answer will be: $(x+m)(x+n)$.

Example 1

Factor $x^2 + 10x + 24$

If we expand $(x+6)(x+4)$ we get the 4 combinations as shown in the diagram:

	x	6
x	x^2	$6x$
4	$4x$	24

$$\therefore \; (x+6)(x+4) = x^2 + 6x + 4x + 24$$
$$= x^2 + 10x + 24$$

Notice the coefficient of 'x' is the sum '$6+4$' and at the same time the last term is the product '6×4'. Therefore to factor $x^2 + 10x + 24$, we have to find two numbers which add to the

1

middle term's coefficient, '10', and at the same time multiply to the last term, '24'. This **sum and product** fact is always used to factor trinomials of the form $x^2 + bx + c$.

FACTORING a$x^2 + bx + c$, $a \neq 1$, *USING TRIAL AND ERROR*

Much factoring involves guesswork and hunches which are then tested out to see if they can simplify the problem.

Example 1

Factor $2x^2 + 7x + 6$

Sum and product factoring cannot be used because the first term is not 'x^2'. So let's try a different process of factoring using **trial and error**. Draw a vertical line. To the left of the line write in a vertical column – two numbers that multiply to the coefficient of the first term, i.e. 2x1 with the larger number on top. To the right of the line write in a vertical column all the combinations of two numbers which multiply to the last term including the reverse orders, i.e. 6x1; 1x6; 3x2; and 2x3 as shown in the diagram.

$$
\begin{array}{c|cccc}
2 & 6 & 1 & 3 & 2 \\
1 & 1 & 6 & 2 & 3
\end{array}
$$

Choose the column from the left side and the first column from the right side of the line as shown below.

$$
\boxed{\begin{array}{c} 2 \\ 1 \end{array}} \ \bigg| \ \boxed{\begin{array}{c} 6 \\ 1 \end{array}} \ \begin{array}{ccc} 1 & 3 & 2 \\ 6 & 2 & 3 \end{array}
$$

Multiply the diagonal numbers of these two columns and observe if they can be combined in some way to add to the coefficient of the middle term of the question, 7. In this case, we see that $2 \times 1 = 2$ and $6 \times 1 = 6$ gives the numbers 2 and 6 which cannot be combined to add to 7.

Choose the column from the left side and the second column from the right side and repeat the process.

$$
\boxed{\begin{array}{c} 2 \\ 1 \end{array}} \ \bigg| \ \begin{array}{c} 6 \\ 1 \end{array} \ \boxed{\begin{array}{c} 1 \\ 6 \end{array}} \ \begin{array}{cc} 3 & 2 \\ 2 & 3 \end{array}
$$

The diagonal products are $2 \times 6 = 12$ and $1 \times 1 = 1$. The numbers 12 and 1 cannot combine to give a seven.

Choose the column from the left side with the third column from the right side of the line.

$$\begin{array}{c|cccc} \boxed{\begin{array}{c}2\\1\end{array}} & 6 & 1 & \boxed{\begin{array}{c}3\\2\end{array}} & \begin{array}{c}2\\3\end{array} \end{array}$$

The diagonal products are $2 \times 2 = 4$ and $1 \times 3 = 3$. The numbers 4 and 3 can be added to give 7. The answer is then found in the rows of these two columns. The first row has the numbers 2 and 3 in that order, therefore the first factor is $(2x+3)$. The second row has the numbers 1 and 2 in that order, therefore the second factor is $(1x+2)$. The answer is then $(2x+3)(x+2)$.

Example 2

Factor $8x^2 + 13x - 6$

Draw a vertical line. To the left of the line write in vertical columns all two number combinations that multiply to the coefficient of the first term, 8, with the larger number on top, i.e. 8×1 and 4×2. To the right of the line write in vertical columns all two number combinations that multiply to the last term of the question, 6, as shown in the diagram below:

$$\begin{array}{cc|cccc} 8 & 4 & 6 & 1 & 3 & 2 \\ 1 & 2 & 1 & 6 & 2 & 3 \end{array}$$

Choose the first column to the left of the line. Check each column to the right of the line with this first column to see if the diagonal products can combine in any way to give the coefficient of the middle term, 13. We see with the first column on each side of the line that the diagonal products are $8 \times 1 = 8$ and $1 \times 6 = 6$, but 8 and 6 cannot combine to be 13 in any way. With the first column to the left of the line and the second column to the right of the line the diagonal products are $8 \times 6 = 48$ and $1 \times 1 = 1$ but 48 and 1 cannot combine to produce 13 in any way.

However in choosing the first column to the left of the line ,and the third column to the right of the line the diagonal products are $8 \times 2 = 16$ and $1 \times 3 = 3$ and $16 - 3 = 13$. To obtain the answer we must put the negative sign on the diagonal product $1 \times 3 = 3$ pairing. Always put the negative sign on the number to the right

3

of the line. Therefore work with $1x-3=-3$ as shown in the diagram below.

$$
\begin{array}{cc|cc|c|c}
\boxed{8} & 4 & 6 & 1 & \boxed{-3} & 2 \\
1 & 2 & 1 & 6 & 2 & 3
\end{array}
$$

The answer is found in the rows of the columns shown above. The first row is an 8 and -3, therefore the first factor is $(8x-3)$. The second row is a 1 and a 2, therefore the second factor is $(1x+2)$. The answer is $(8x-3)(x+2)$. To check, multiply it out:

$$
\begin{aligned}
(8x-3)(x+2) &= 8x^2-3x+16x-6 \\
&= 8x^2+13x-6,
\end{aligned}
$$

this is correct because we have the question back!

Example 3

Factor $\qquad 6x^3-22x^2+12x$

Always factor out the **greatest common factor** first, $6x^3-22x^2+12x=2x(3x^2-11x+6)$. The expression $3x^2-11x+6$ may factor by **trial and error** so place the two numbers which multiply to the coefficient of the first term, $3 \times 1=3$, in a vertical column with the larger number on top to the left of a vertical line.

Place all orderings of pairs of numbers which multiply to the

$$
\begin{array}{c|cccc}
3 & 6 & 1 & 3 & 2 \\
1 & 1 & 6 & 2 & 3
\end{array}
$$

last term, 6, to the right of the line, i.e. 6×1, 1×6, 3×2, and 2×3.

As we have done before check each column to the right of the line with the column of numbers to the left of the line for diagonal products which can combine in some way to the coefficient of the middle term, -11. Only the last column to the

$$
\begin{array}{c|ccc|c}
\boxed{3} & 6 & 1 & 3 & \boxed{2} \\
\boxed{1} & 1 & 6 & 2 & \boxed{3}
\end{array}
$$

right of the line will do this.

The factoring for $3x^2-11x+6$ is in the rows, $3x^2-11x+6=(3x-2)(x-3)$. The overall answer is $2x(3x-2)(x-3)$.

How to factor trinomials of the form $ax^2 + bx + c$, $a \neq 1$ using trial and error

To factor $ax^2 + bx + c$, $a \neq 1$ try the following:

1. List all pairs of numbers which multiply to 'a' in vertical columns with the larger number on top to the left of a vertical line.

2. List all pairs of positive numbers which multiply to 'c' to the right of the vertical line in all possible orders.

3. Pick one column from each side of the line. Multiply the numbers in the diagonals of these two columns to produce two numbers, one from each diagonal. If these two diagonal product numbers cannot combine in some way to equal 'b' then try again with another two columns, one from each side of the line.

4. When the correct two columns are found, place the negative signs, if necessary, to the right of the line so that the diagonal products combine to give the value 'b'. The answer is then found in the rows of these two columns, each row representing one of the factors.

FACTORING A PERFECT SQUARE TRINOMIAL

When the first and last terms of a trinomial are squares, we have an easy procedure to find factors.

Example 1

Factor $x^2 - 6x + 9$

	x	−3
x	x^2	$-3x$
−3	$-3x$	9

Expand the square of the binomial $(x-3)^2$.
From the diagram we see that

$$(x-3)^2 = (x-3)(x-3)$$
$$= x^2 - 3x - 3x + 9$$
$$= x^2 - 6x + 9$$

Notice that the first and third terms of the answer, x^2 and 9, are squares of the two terms, 'x' and '3'. Because the middle two terms of the expansion are both $-3x$, the middle term of the answer is twice this, $-6x$. To factor $x^2 - 6x + 9$ we see that the first and third terms are squares of 'x' and '3' and that the middle term is twice the product of 'x' and '3'. The answer then must be the square of a binomial with a negative sign, $(x-3)^2$. We call this process factoring a **perfect square trinomial**.

We have the following formulas for factoring a **perfect square trinomial**:

$$x^2 + 2xy + y^2 = (x+y)^2$$
$$x^2 - 2xy + y^2 = (x-y)^2$$

Example 2

Factor $\quad 4x^2 + 12x + 9$

The first and third terms are squares of '$2x$' and '3' and the middle term is twice the product of '$2x$' and '3' i.e. $2(2x)(3)=12x$, so we must factor by using the first formula for a perfect square trinomial. The answer is $(2x+3)^2$.

Example 3

Factor $\quad x^2 - 10x + 25$

The first and third terms are squares of 'x' and '5' and the middle term is double the product of 'x' and '5' i.e. $10x$, therefore we must factor by using the formula for a **perfect square trinomial**. The answer is $(x-5)^2$.

Example 4

Factor $\quad 64x^2 + 16x + 1$

The first and third terms are squares of '$8x$' and '1' and the middle term is double the product of '$8x$' and '1' i.e. $16x$, therefore we must factor by using the second formula for a **perfect square trinomial**. The answer is $(8x+1)^2$.

Example 5

Factor $\quad 98x^3 - 168x^2 + 72x$

There is no square which gives 96 or 72, so, in this case, we factor by the **greatest common factor** first. The **greatest common factor** is '$2x$'.

$\therefore 98x^3 - 168x^2 + 72x = 2x(49x^2 - 84x + 36)$

Now we factor $49x^2 - 84x + 36$. The first and third terms of the expression $49x^2 - 84x + 36$ are squares of '$7x$' and '6' and the middle term is double the product of '$7x$' and '6', i.e. $2(7x)(6)=84x$, therefore we must factor by using the formula for a **perfect square trinomial**.

$$\therefore 49x^2 - 84x + 36 = (7x - 6)^2.$$

When we bring back the '$2x$', the full answer is $2x(7x-6)^2$.

FACTORING A DIFFERENCE OF SQUARES

Example 1

Factor $\quad 49x^2 - 16$

Expand $\quad (7x+4)(7x-4)$

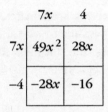

From the diagram we see
$$(7x+4)(7x-4) = 49x^2 + 28x - 28x - 16$$
$$= 49x^2 - 16$$

When an expression of this type is expanded, the two middle terms cancel out giving us a two term answer. This is called a **difference of squares** of the terms in each expression of the question, $(7x)^2 - 4^2$. Therefore to factor $49x^2 - 16$, the answer is the sum of the square roots of $49x^2$ and 16, $(7x+4)$, multiplied by the difference of the square roots, $(7x-4)$, i.e. $(7x+4)(7x-4)$.

HOW TO FACTOR A DIFFERENCE OF SQUARES

If we see a difference of two terms and each term can be put in the form of a square, $a^2 - b^2$, then factor by using the following process:

(i) Write the square roots of each term in two pair of brackets, (a   b)(a   b).

(ii) Separate the square roots with a 'plus' sign in the first bracket pair, and a 'negative' sign in the second, $(a+b)(a-b)$.

Example 2

Factor $\quad 100 - 4x^2$

Always factor by the **greatest common factor** first: $100 - 4x^2 = 4(25 - x^2)$. Since $25 - x^2 = 5^2 - x^2$, which is a **difference of squares**, make two pair of brackets with the square roots '5' and 'x' in each, $(5 \ x)(5 \ x)$. Put opposite signs in each pair, $(5+x)(5-x)$. The answer with the **common factor** is $4(5+x)(5-x)$.

Example 3

Factor $\quad x^2 - 8x + 16 - y^2$

Observe that the first three terms is the **perfect square trinomial**, $(x-4)^2$. We now have $x^2 - 8x + 16 - y^2 = (x-4)^2 - y^2$.

We see two squares separated by a subtraction sign giving a **difference of squares**.

The square root of $(x-4)^2$, $\sqrt{(x-4)^2}$ is $(x-4)$.

Write the square roots in two pair of square brackets in the following way: $[(x-4) \ y][(x-4) \ y]$. Put opposite signs in each pair: $[(x-4)+y][(x-4)-y]$.

Since innermost brackets are always removed when factoring the answer is $(x-4+y)(x-4-y)$.

Example 4

Factor $\quad 81z^2 - 9x^2 + 30xy - 25y^2$

First factor out the negative sign in the last three terms: $-9x^2 + 30xy - 25y^2 = -(9x^2 - 30xy + 25y^2)$

Then observe that the expression $9x^2 - 30xy + 25y^2$ is a **perfect square trinomial**, $(3x-5y)^2$. We have left a **difference of squares**:

$$81z^2 - 9x^2 + 30xy - 25y^2 = 81z^2 - (9x^2 - 30xy + 25y^2)$$
$$= 81z^2 - (3x-5y)^2$$

The square roots of $81z^2$ and $(3x-5y)^2$ are $9z$ and $(3x-5y)$ respectively. Write two pair of square brackets with these square roots inside: $[9z \ (3x-5y)][9z \ (3x-5y)]$. Put opposite signs in each pair and remove innermost brackets to give the answer in simplified form:

$$[9z+ (3x-5y)][9z- \ (3x-5y)] = (9z+3x-5y)(9z-3x+5y).$$

To check, multiply it out:

$$(9z+3x-5y)(9z-3x+5y)=$$
$$81z^2-27zx+45zy+27xz-9x^2+15xy-45yz+15yx-25y^2$$
$$= 81z^2-9x^2+30xy-25y^2$$

this is correct because
we have the question back!

FACTORING BY A SUM AND DIFFERENCE OF CUBES

Example 1

Factor $\qquad 27x^3-8$

Expand $(3x-2)(9x^2+6x+4)$ as shown in the diagram below.

	$9x^2$	$6x$	4
$3x$	$27x^2$	$18x^2$	$12x$
-2	$-18x^2$	$-12x$	-8

From the diagram we see:
$$(3x-2)(9x^2+6x+4) = 27x^3+18x^2-18x^2+12x-12x-8$$
$$= 27x^3-8$$

Notice that $(3x)^3=27x^3$ and $2^3=8$, therefore the cube roots of the two terms in the answer are $3x$ and 2. These two cube roots are found in the first expression of the expansion question, $(3x-2)$. Also notice that the squares of these 'cube roots', $9x^2$ and 4, form the first and third terms of the second factor of the expansion, $(9x^2+6x+4)$. The middle term of the second expression, $6x$, is the product of the cube roots with the sign opposite to the sign of the first factor $(3x-2)$.

To factor a **difference of cubes**, $(3x)^3-2^3$, the first factor expression of the answer is always the difference of the cube roots, $(3x-2)$. The second is always a three term expression in which the first and the third terms are the squares of the 'cube roots', $9x^2$ and 4, and the middle term is the product of the 'cube roots', $6x$. The sign is opposite to the first expression, $(9x^2+6x+4)$. The answer is: $27x^3-8 = (3x-2)(9x^2+6x+4)$.

HOW TO FACTOR A DIFFERENCE OF CUBES

If we see a difference of two terms and each term can be expressed as a cube, x^3-y^3, then the answer will be two expressions you can find in the following way:

(i)   The first expression is a difference of the cube roots, $(x-y)$.

(ii) The second expression will have three terms. The first and third terms will be the squares of the cube roots. The middle term will be the product of the cube roots with the sign opposite to the first expression, (x^2+xy+y^2). The answer will be $x^3-y^3 = (x-y)(x^2+xy+y^2)$.

HOW TO FACTOR A SUM OF CUBES

If we see a sum of two terms and each term can be expressed as a cube, x^3+y^3, then the answer will be two expressions like this:

(i)   The first expression is a sum of the cube roots, $(x+y)$.

(ii) The second expression will have three terms. The first and third terms will be the squares of the cube roots. The middle term will be the product of the cube roots with the sign opposite to the first expression, (x^2-xy+y^2). The answer will be $x^3-y^3 = (x+y)(x^2-xy+y^2)$.

Example 2

Factor $125x^3+64$

The expression above is a **sum of cubes**, $(5x)^3+4^3$. The first factor is the sum of the cube roots, $(5x+4)$. The second factor has three terms, the first and third of which are the squares of the cube roots, $25x^2$ and 16. The middle term is the product of the cube roots, $(5x)(4)=20x$, with the sign opposite to the first factor,

$-20x$. The answer is $125x^3 + 64 = (5x+4)(25x^2 - 20x + 16)$.

To check, multiply it out:
$$(5x+4)(25x^2 - 20x + 16)$$
$$= 125x^3 - 100x^2 + 80x + 100x^2 - 80x + 64$$
$$= 125x^3 + 64$$

Example 3

Factor $\quad x^6 - y^6$

The expression is a **difference of cubes**, $(x^2)^3 - (y^2)^3$. The first expression is the difference of the cube roots, $(x^2 - y^2)$. The second expression has three terms, the first and third of which are squares of the cube roots, $(x^2)^2 = x^4$ and $(y^2)^2 = y^4$. The middle term is the product of the cube roots with the sign opposite the first expression, x^2y^2. The answer is:
$$x^6 - y^6 = (x^2 - y^2)(x^4 + x^2y^2 + y^4)$$
$$= (x+y)(x-y)(x^4 + x^2y^2 + y^4)$$
Note that the first expression is a **difference of squares**.

Example 4

Factor $\quad (x+2y)^3 + (x-2y)^3$

The expression is a **sum of cubes**. The cube roots are also expressions, $(x+2y)$ and $(x-2y)$. The first expression of the answer is the sum of the cube roots, $[(x+2y)+(x-2y)]$. The second expression of the answer has three terms, the first and third of which are squares of the cube roots, $(x+2y)^2$ and $(x-2y)^2$. The middle term is the product of the cube roots with the sign opposite the first expression, $-(x+2y)(x-2y)$. Then we expand and simplify innermost brackets. The answer is:

$$(x+2y)^3 + (x-2y)^3$$
$$= [(x+2y)+(x-2y)][(x+2y)^2 - (x+2y)(x-2y)+(x-2y)^2]$$
$$= [x+2y+x-2y][x^2+4xy+4y^2 - (x^2-4y^2)+x^2-4xy+4y^2]$$
$$= 2x(x^2+4xy+4y^2-x^2+4y^2+x^2-4xy-4y^2)$$
$$= 2x(x^2+12y^2)$$

PRACTICE EXERCISE

Factor each of the following:

a) $xy+2x-y-2$

b) $ad-3bd-ab+3b^2+ac-3bc$

c) $x^2+12x-28$

d) $x^2-14x+48$

e) $2x^3+12x^2-32x$

f) $(x^2-3x)^2-14(x^2-3x)+40$

g) $100x^2+180x+81$

h) $3x^5y-42x^4y+147x^3y$

i) $2x^2-7x-15$

j) $24x^2+13x-2$

k) $36x^7-100x^5$

l) $x^4-13x^2y^2+36y^4$

m) $x^2-10x+25-y^2$

n) $25y^2-9x^2+12x-4$

o) x^3-216

p) $108x^3+500$

q) x^6+y^6

r) $(3x-1)^3-(3x+1)^3$

CHAPTER TWO

Division of polynomials

LONG DIVISION

Division of polynomials looks complicated, but the process is actually very similar to the long division everyone does in the junior grades. The basic concept is to keep dividing until you get a simple remainder. If you happen to be missing a term, the trick is to use a placeholder.

Example 1

Divide $(2x^2 + 5x + 5) \div (2x - 3)$.

The process of long polynomial division can be compared to the simple process of dividing 36 into 872.

$$
\begin{array}{r}
24 \\
36\overline{)872} \\
\underline{72} \\
152 \\
\underline{144} \\
8
\end{array}
$$

Steps

1. Divide 36 into 87 for the nearest multiple below 87, write 2 on top of 7 (ten's column), write the product 2×36 below 87.

2. Subtract to find the remainder. Write 15 below 72 and bring down the next number, 2, beside the remainder 15.

3. Divide 36 into 152 for the lowest multiple below 152, write 4 on top of the units digit 2, write the product 4×36 below 152.

14

4. Subtract to find the remainder. Write 8 below 144. Since there are no more numbers to bring down the answer is

$$\frac{872}{36} = 24\frac{8}{36} = 24\frac{2}{9}$$

5. Check that $36 \times 24 + 8 = 872$.

Long Division of Poynomials

Divide $(2x^2 + 5x - 5) \div (2x - 3)$

$$
\begin{array}{r}
x + 4 \\
2x - 3 \enclose{longdiv}{2x^2 + 5x - 5} \\
\underline{2x^2 - 3x} \\
8x - 5 \\
\underline{8x - 12} \\
7
\end{array}
$$

Steps

1. Divide the first term of $2x - 3$ into the first term of $2x^2 + 5x - 5$, i.e. divide $2x$ into $2x^2$. Write x on top of $5x$ (like terms), write the product $x(2x - 3)$ i.e. $2x^2 - 3x$ below $2x^2 + 5x$.
2. Subtract to find the remainder of $8x$. Write $8x$ below $-3x$ and bring down the next term, -5. Write -5 beside the remainder.
3. Divide $2x$ into $8x$. Write 4 on top of -5 (like terms), write the product $4(2x - 3)$ i.e. $8x - 12$ below $8x - 5$.
4. Subtract to find the remainder. Write 7 below -12. Since there are no more terms to bring down the answer is: $(2x^2 + 5x - 5) \div (2x - 3) = x + 4 +$ remainder 7.
5. Check that $(2x - 3)(x + 4) + 7 = 2x^2 + 5x - 5$.

Example 2

Divide $(18x - 19x^2 + 6x^3 - 22) \div (2x - 5)$

$$\begin{array}{r} 3x^2-2x+4 \\ 2x-5\overline{\smash{\big)}\,6x^3-19x^2+18x-22} \\ \underline{6x^3-15x^2} \\ -4x^2+18x \\ \underline{-4x^2+10x} \\ 8x-22 \\ \underline{8x-20} \\ -2 \end{array}$$

Remember terms must always be in descending powers:
$6x^3-19x^2+18x-22$
Therefore $(6x^3-19x^2+18x-22)\div(2x-5)$
$$= 3x^2-2x+4+ \text{ remainder } -2.$$
To check, expand and simplify:
$$(2x-5)(3x^2-2x+4)-2$$
$$=6x^3-4x^2+8x-15x^2+10x-20x-2$$
$$=6x^3-19x^2+18x-22,$$
this is correct because we have
the expression of the question back!

Example 3

Divide $(6x^3-21-5x^2)$ by $(3x-7)$

Terms must be in descending powers and the **placeholder** '$0x$' can be used to fill in the missing power.

$$\begin{array}{r} 2x^2-3x+7 \\ 3x-7\overline{\smash{\big)}\,6x^3-\ 5x^2+0x-21} \\ \underline{6x^3-14x^2} \\ -9x^2+\ 0x \\ \underline{-9x^2+21x} \\ 21x-21 \\ \underline{21x-21} \\ 0 \end{array}$$

$\therefore\ (6x^3-21-5x^2)\div(3x-7)=2x^2-3x+7+ \text{ remainder } 0.$

PRACTICE EXERCISE

1. Divide
   a) $(x^3 - 8x^2 + 3x + 2) \div (x + 1)$
   b) $(3x^4 + 5x^3 - 10x^2 + 6) \div (x + 5)$
   c) $(8x^3 - 12 - 26x) \div (2x + 1)$

2. Two factors of $x^4 + 2x^3 - 13x^2 - 38x - 24$ are $(x + 2)$ and $(x + 3)$. Find the other factors.

CHAPTER THREE

The remainder theorem

The Remainder Theorem is a simple way to find the remainder when dividing polynomials. It permits you to skip the full long division, and also to work backwards when you are told what the remainder is.

The Remainder Theorem

1. When a polynomial, $P(x)$, is divided by $(x-b)$ and the remainder contains no terms in x, then the remainder is $P(b)$.
2. When a polynomial, $P(x)$, is divided by $(ax-b)$, and the remainder contains no term in x, then the remainder is $P(\frac{a}{b})$.

Example 1

Find the remainder using the **Remainder Theorem** for $(2x^3 - 13x^2 + 19x + 7) \div (2x - 3)$.

If $2x - 3 = 0$, then $x = \dfrac{3}{2}$.

Using the Remainder Theorem we can substitute in the equation to find the remainder:

18

$$P(\tfrac{3}{2}) = 2(\tfrac{3}{2})^3 - 13(\tfrac{3}{2})^2 + 19(\tfrac{3}{2}) + 7$$

$$= \frac{27}{4} - \frac{117}{4} + \frac{57}{2} + 7$$

$$= \frac{27 - 117 + 114 + 28}{4}$$

$$= \frac{52}{4}$$

$$= 13$$

Example 2

When $(x^3 + 3x^2 - kx + 10)$ is divided by $(x - 5)$ the remainder is 15. Find the value of k.

Since $x - 5 = 0$ when $x = 5$, by the **Remainder Theorem** $P(5)$ gives the remainder. Therefore $P(5) = 15$ but $P(5) = 5^3 + 3 \cdot 5^2 - 5k + 10$. We have $125 + 75 - 5k + 10 = 15$, from which it follows that $k = 39$.

PRACTICE EXERCISE

1. Find the remainder using the Remainder Theorem:

   a) $(2x^3 - 4x^2 - x + 4) \div (x + 5)$
   b) $(2x^3 + 3x^2 - 7x - 5) \div (2x + 5)$

2. When $(2x^2 + kx + 2)$ is divided by $(2x + 1)$ the remainder is 5. Find the value of k.

The factor
theorem

The Factor Theorem is a way to factor more difficult expressions than we cannot ordinarily tackle with the other types of factoring. Basically, it uses a form of trial-and-error to solve a problem.

The Factor Theorem

A polynomial (with highest power x^3 here, but works for any power in integers) $P(x) = dx^3 + cx^2 + bx + a$ where a, b, c and d are real numbers has $(x - q)$ as a factor if and only if $P(q) = 0$. The possible values of 'q' will always be chosen from the fractions:

$$\frac{\text{any divisor of 'a'}}{\text{any divisor of 'd'}}$$

If $d = 1$, then the possible values of 'q' will be chosen from any divisor of the constant term, 'a'.

Let's look at the following example. The question asks you to factor $x^3 - 3x^2 - 4x + 12$, in which $a = 12$ and $d = 1$. What this means, in simple language, is that if you find by trial and error that one of the positive or negative divisors of 12 gives a zero when substituted into the expression, in this case '2' is such a number, then $(x-2)$ must be a factor of the polynomial. (The case where 'd' is not one will be explained in example two.)

Example 1

Factor $x^3 - 3x^2 - 4x + 12$.

The constant term, 12, is divisible by ±1, ±2, ±3, etc. Start substituting the positive divisors of 12 starting from the lowest ones into $P(x) = x^3 - 3x^2 - 4x + 12$ until the substitution gives numbers which can add to zero. The results of trying $x = 1$ and $x = 2$ are $P(1) = 1 - 3 - 4 + 12 = 6$ and $P(2) = 8 - 12 - 8 + 12 = 0$. Here the value $x = 2$ gives the first zero remainder, therefore $(x - 2)$ is a factor of the polynomial by the Remainder Theorem. By **long division:**

$$\therefore \ x^3 - 3x^2 - 4x + 12 \ = \ (x - 2)(x^2 - x - 6)$$
$$= \ (x - 2)(x + 2)(x - 3).$$

To check, multiply it out:

$$(x - 2)(x + 2)(x - 3) \ = \ (x^2 - 4)(x - 3)$$
$$= \ x^3 - 3x^2 - 4x + 12,$$
this is correct because
we have the question back!

Example 2

Factor $4x^3 + 16x^2 + 9x - 9$.

Here, $a = -9$, $b = 9$, $c = 16$ and $d = 4$. The possible values of q are any divisor of -9 divided by any divisor of 4.

The divisors of $\dfrac{-9}{4}$ are $\dfrac{\pm 1, \pm 3}{\pm 1, \pm 2, \pm 4}$ so we first try $x = \dfrac{1}{1}$ and $x = \dfrac{1}{2}$ which gives the following two values:

$P(1) = 4 + 16 + 9 - 9 = 20,$

$$P\left(\frac{1}{2}\right) = 4\left(\frac{1}{2}\right)^3 + 16\left(\frac{1}{2}\right)^2 + 9\left(\frac{1}{2}\right) - 9 = 0.$$

$P\left(\frac{1}{2}\right) = 0,$ therefore $\left(x - \frac{1}{2}\right)$ is a factor of the polynomial, i.e.

$2\left(x - \frac{1}{2}\right) = (2x - 1)$ since any multiple of $\left(x - \frac{1}{2}\right)$ is also a factor.

By **long division** we have:

$$\left(4x^3 + 16x^2 + 9x - 9\right) \div (2x - 1) = 2x^2 + 9x + 9.$$

$$\therefore \quad \left(4x^3 + 16x^2 + 9x - 9\right) = \left(2x - 1\right)\left(2x^2 + 9x + 9\right)$$

$$= (2x - 1)(x + 3)(2x + 3)$$

To check, we multiply it out:

$$(2x - 1)(x + 3)(2x + 3) = (2x^2 + 5x - 3)(2x + 3)$$

$$= 4x^3 + 16x^2 + 9x - 9,$$

this is correct because

we have the question back!

PRACTICE EXERCISE

1. Factor each of the following
   a) $x^3 - 6x^2 - x + 30$
   b) $2x^3 - 3x^2 - 11x + 6$

2. Find k so that $x^3 - 4x^2 - 2x + k$ has $(x - 3)$ as a factor.

CHAPTER FIVE

Completing the square

Completing the square is a common procedure in algebra. It comes out of the simple fact that many algebraic equations are simple squares, like $(x+3)^2$, which are then modified by an added digit like +5 or −5. We frequently find this in graphing where, for instance, a parabola will be moved vertically up or down on a graph by adding a number. Solving a problem by completing the square may look difficult, but it's really quite simple.

Example 1

Express $y = x^2 - 6x + 5$ in the form $y = (x-p)^2 + q$.

Expand $(x-3)^2$. We see that $(x-3)^2 = x^2 - 6x + 9$ is a **perfect square trinomial**, thus the first and third terms of the expansion are squares of 'x' and '3' and the middle term is double the product, $-6x$. If we want to **complete the square** for $x^2 - 6x$ we must add half the coefficient of x squared, $[\frac{1}{2}(-6)]^2$ which is 9. To **complete the square** for $y = x^2 - 6x + 5$, we leave a space before the 5, $y = x^2 - 6x\ \ 5$, then add and subtract half the coefficient of x squared, 9.

The answer is
$$y = x^2 - 6x + 9 - 9 + 5$$
$$= (x^2 - 6x + 9) - 9 + 5$$
$$= (x-3)^2 - 4$$

23

How to put $y = x^2 + bx + c$
Into the form $y = (x-p)^2 + q$

1. **Complete the square** by adding (half the coefficient of x) squared to the first two terms and at the same time subtracting this number from the remaining term.
2. Write the first three terms as a **perfect square trinomial** while simplifying the last two terms.

Example 2

Express $y = x^2 + 3x - 8$ in the form $y = (x-p)^2 + q$.

Complete the square using the first two terms by adding and subtracting half the coefficient of x, squared $\left[\dfrac{1}{2}(3) \right]^2 = \left(\dfrac{3}{2} \right)^2 = \dfrac{9}{4}$.

$$\therefore \quad x^2 + 3x + \frac{9}{4} - \frac{9}{4} - 8 = \left(x^2 + 3x + \frac{9}{4} \right) - \frac{9}{4} - 8$$

$$= \left(x + \frac{3}{2} \right)^2 - \frac{9}{4} - \frac{32}{4}$$

$$= \left(x + \frac{3}{2} \right)^2 - \frac{41}{4}.$$

Example 3

Express $y = 2x^2 - 12x + 11$ in the form $y = a\left(x - p \right)^2 + q$.

Always start off by making the coefficient of the x^2 term '1'. To do this we divide both sides of the equation by two:

24

$$\therefore \quad \frac{y}{2} = \frac{2x^2 - 12x + 11}{2}$$

$$\therefore \quad \frac{y}{2} = x^2 - 6x + \frac{11}{2}. \quad \text{Complete the square on the right side}$$

$$\therefore \quad \frac{y}{2} = x^2 - 6x + 9 - 9 + \frac{11}{2}$$

$$\therefore \quad \frac{y}{2} = \left(x - 3\right)^2 - \frac{18}{2} + \frac{11}{2}$$

$$\therefore \quad \frac{y}{2} = \left(x - 3\right)^2 - \frac{7}{2}$$

$$\therefore \quad \frac{y}{2} = 2\left(x - 3\right)^2 - 7$$

$$\therefore \quad 2\left(\frac{y}{2}\right) = 2\left[2\left(x - 3\right)^2 - 7\right]$$

$$\therefore \quad y = 4\left(x - 3\right)^2 - 14$$

How to put $y = ax^2 + bx + c$ Into the form $y = a(x - p)^2 + q$

1. Divide both sides of the equation by 'a' to give $\dfrac{y}{a} = x^2 + \dfrac{b}{a}x + \dfrac{c}{a}$

2. **Complete the square** on the right side.

3. Multiply both sides of the equation by 'a'.

Example 4

Express $y = \dfrac{2}{3}x^2 - 3x + 9$ in the form $y = a\left(x - p\right)^2 + q$.

Divide both sides of the equation by $\dfrac{2}{3}$ i.e. multiply both sides of the equation by $\dfrac{3}{2}$:

$$\therefore \quad \frac{3}{2}(y) = \frac{3}{2}\left(\frac{2}{3}x^2 - 3x + 9\right)$$

$$\therefore \quad \frac{3y}{2} = x^2 - \frac{3}{2}(3x) + \frac{3}{2}(9)$$

$$\therefore \quad \frac{3y}{2} = x^2 - \frac{9x}{2} + \frac{27}{2}$$

Complete the square on the right side by adding and subtracting (half the coefficient of x) squared,

$$\left[\frac{1}{2}\left(\frac{9}{2}\right)\right]^2 = \left(\frac{9}{4}\right)^2 = \frac{81}{16}.$$

$$\therefore \quad \frac{3y}{2} = x^2 - \frac{9x}{2} + \frac{81}{16} - \frac{81}{16} + \frac{27}{2}$$

$$\therefore \quad \frac{3y}{2} = \left(x - \frac{9}{4}\right)^2 + \frac{135}{16},$$

then multiply both sides of the equation by $\frac{2}{3}$.

$$\therefore \quad \frac{2}{3}\left(\frac{3y}{2}\right) = \frac{2}{3}\left(\left(x - \frac{9}{4}\right)^2 + \frac{135}{16}\right)$$

$$\therefore \quad y = \frac{2}{3}\left(x - \frac{9}{4}\right)^2 + \frac{45}{8}.$$

PRACTICE EXERCISE

Express each of the following in the form $y = a(x - p)^2 + q$:

a) $y = x^2 - 18x + 21$
b) $y = 3x^2 - 18x + 49$

c) $y = 2x^2 - 5x + 6$
d) $y = \frac{3}{4}x^2 - 4x + 8$

CHAPTER SIX

Quadratic formula

The Quadratic Formula can be used to solve many problems in math, physics and the physical sciences. It begins, of course, with math. The Quadratic Formula to find the two roots of a quadratic equation is based on ways to find the x–intercepts of the graph of a parabola:

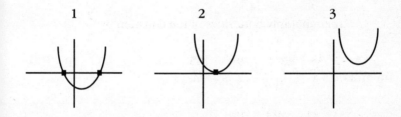

1   2   3

Diagram 1 – two x-intercepts (the two roots are real and distinct).
Diagram 2 – one x-intercept (the two roots are real and equal).
Diagram 3 – no x-intercept (the two roots are not real).

The **Quadratic Formula** is one that you can figure out for yourself (though it's usually better just to memorize it). It begins as a way to solve the equation to **complete the square**. In general to solve $ax^2 + bx + c = 0$, we **complete the square**.

First divide the equation through by 'a', $x^2 + \dfrac{b}{a}x + \dfrac{c}{a} = 0$

then add and subtract half the coefficient of x, squared.

$$\left[\frac{1}{2}\left(\frac{b}{a}\right)\right]^2 = \left(\frac{b}{2a}\right)^2 = \frac{b^2}{4a^2}$$

$$\therefore \quad \left(x^2 + \frac{b}{a}x + \frac{b^2}{4a^2}\right) - \frac{b^2}{4a^2} + \frac{c}{a} = 0$$

$$\therefore \quad \left(x + \frac{b}{2a}\right)^2 = \frac{b^2}{4a^2} - \frac{c}{a}$$

$$\therefore \quad \left(x + \frac{b}{2a}\right)^2 = \frac{b^2 - 4ac}{4a^2}, \text{ take square roots on both sides}$$

$$\therefore \quad x + \frac{b}{2a} = \pm\sqrt{\frac{b^2 - 4ac}{4a^2}}$$

$$\therefore \quad x + \frac{b}{2a} = \pm\frac{\sqrt{b^2 - 4ac}}{2a}$$

$$\therefore \quad x = -\frac{b}{2a} \pm \frac{\sqrt{b^2 - 4ac}}{2a}$$

As a simplified fraction we now have the **quadratic formula**:

The Quadratic Formula

If $ax^2 + bx + c = 0$, then $x = \dfrac{-b \pm \sqrt{b^2 - 4ac}}{2a}$.

We call $b^2 - 4ac$ the **discriminant, D,** because the value of this expression determines how many solutions there are in real numbers i.e. the **nature of the roots**:

Nature of the Roots of
$$ax^2 + bx + c = 0$$

Let the discriminant, $D = b^2 - 4ac$, then

(i) if $D > 0$, there are two distinct real roots (two solutions).
(ii) if $D = 0$, the roots are real and equal (one solution).
(iii) if $D < 0$, there are no real roots (no solutions).

Example 1

Determine the nature of the roots and solve $3x^2 - 5x - 1 = 0$.

First **complete the square** on the left side of the equation by first dividing by 3,

$$\frac{3x^2 - 5x - 1}{3} = \frac{0}{3}, \quad \therefore x^2 - \frac{5}{3}x - \frac{1}{3} = 0.$$

$$\left[\frac{1}{2}\left(\frac{5}{3}\right)\right]^2 = \left(\frac{5}{6}\right)^2 = \frac{25}{36} \quad \text{to the left side.}$$

$$\therefore \quad \left(x^2 - \frac{5}{3}x + \frac{25}{36}\right) - \frac{25}{36} - \frac{1}{3} = 0$$

$$\therefore \quad \left(x - \frac{5}{6}\right)^2 - \frac{37}{36} = 0$$

$$\therefore \quad \left(x - \frac{5}{6}\right)^2 = \frac{37}{36}, \quad \text{then take square roots on both sides}$$

$$\therefore \quad \sqrt{\left(x - \frac{5}{6}\right)^2} = \pm\sqrt{\frac{37}{36}}$$

$$\therefore \quad x - \frac{5}{6} = \pm\frac{\sqrt{37}}{6}$$

$$\therefore \quad x = \frac{5}{6} \pm \frac{\sqrt{37}}{6}$$

$$\therefore \quad x = \frac{5 \pm \sqrt{37}}{6}$$

$$\therefore \quad x = \frac{5 + \sqrt{37}}{6} \quad \text{or} \quad x = \frac{5 - \sqrt{37}}{6},$$

therefore there are two real and distinct roots.

Example 1 Using the Quadratic Formula

In example one, $a = 3$, $b = -5$, $c = -1$, so we see that $D = (-5)^2 - 4(3)(-1) = 37$, which is a positive value, so there are two distinct real roots.

$$\therefore \quad x = \frac{-(-5) \pm \sqrt{(-5)^2 - 4(3)(-1)}}{2(3)} = \frac{5 \pm \sqrt{25 + 12}}{6} = \frac{5 \pm \sqrt{37}}{6}$$

Therefore the two roots are $x = \frac{5 + \sqrt{37}}{6}$ and $x = \frac{5 - \sqrt{37}}{6}$.

Example 2

Determine the nature of the roots and solve

$$x^2 - \frac{x}{2} + 2 = 0$$

First remove fractions in the equation by multiplying by 2 to give $2(x^2 - \frac{x}{2} + 2) = 2(0)$

$\therefore 2x^2 - x + 4 = 0$. We have $a = 2$, $b = -1$, $c = 4$ and so $D = (-1)^2 - 4(2)(4) = -31$, which is a negative value, there are no real roots.

Example 3

Determine the nature of the roots and solve $4x^2 - 12x + 9 = 0$.

We have $a = 4$, $b = -12$, $c = 9$, since $D = (12)^2 - 4(4)(9) = 0$, the two roots are real and equal (which means that there is only one solution in real numbers).

$$\therefore \quad x = \frac{-(-12) \pm \sqrt{(12)^2 - 4(4)(9)}}{2(4)}$$

$$= \frac{12 \pm \sqrt{144 - 144}}{8}$$

$$= \frac{12 \pm \sqrt{0}}{8}$$

$$= 1.5$$

Example 4

Determine the nature of the roots and solve .

$$\frac{2}{x} - \frac{3}{5-x} = 3$$

The equation must be put into standard form by removing the fractions first. Multiplying both sides by the lowest common denominator we have:

$$\therefore \quad x(5-x)\left(\frac{2}{x} - \frac{3}{5-x}\right) = 3x(5-x)$$

$$\therefore \quad x(5-x)\left(\frac{2}{x}\right) - x(5-x)\frac{3}{5-x} = 3x(5-x)$$

$$\therefore \quad 2(5-x) - 3x = 15x - 3x^2$$

$$\therefore \quad 3x^2 - 20x + 10 = 0. \quad \text{We have} \quad a = 3, b = -20 \text{ and } c = 10.$$

Since $D = (-20)^2 - 4(3)(10) = 280$ which is a positive number there are two distinct real roots which are

$$\therefore \quad x = \frac{20 \pm \sqrt{(-20)^2 - 4(3)(10)}}{2(3)}$$

$$= \frac{20 \pm \sqrt{280}}{6}$$

$$= \frac{20 \pm 2\sqrt{70}}{6}$$

$$= \frac{10 \pm \sqrt{70}}{3}$$

Example 5

The difference of two numbers is 13 and their product is 300. Find the numbers.

Let the two numbers be represented by 'x' and '$x+13$'.

$\therefore \quad x(x+13) = 300$

$\therefore \quad x^2 + 13x - 300 = 0, \quad a = 1, \ b = 13, \ c = -300.$

By quadratic formula $x = -25$ or $x = 12$.

If $x = -25$, the two numbers are -25 and $-25 + 13 = -12$.

If $x = 12$, the two numbers are 12 and $12 + 13 = 25$.

Example 6

Find two numbers whose sum is 14 and whose product is 24.

Let the two numbers be represented by 'x' and '$14-x$'.

$\therefore \quad x(14 - x) = 24$

$\therefore \quad x^2 - 14x + 24 = 0$

$\therefore \quad a = 1, \ b = -14, \ c = 24.$

By quadratic formula $x = 2$ or $x = 12$.

The two numbers are 2 or 12.

Guidelines to solving applications using the quadratic formula

1. Translate English into algebra using one variable. Use a labeled diagram or chart to help visualize if necessary. Remember to define the variable in a 'let' statement or chart and state the units of the variable.

2. Solve the algebraic equation in the form $ax^2 + bx + c = 0$ by the quadratic formula.

3. Make a complete English statement which answers the question for a conclusion.

Example 7

Two people wish to mow a rectangular lawn 80m x 60m. One will mow a strip of uniform width on the outside equal to half the area of the garden. How wide should the border be?

Let the width of the strip in metres be represented by 'x'.

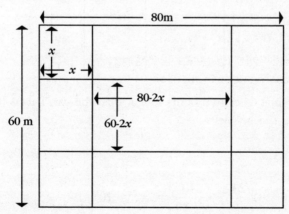

Then the inner rectangle area equals half the area of the entire lawn rectangle.

$$\therefore \quad (80-2x)(60-2x) = \frac{1}{2}(60)(80)$$

$$\therefore \quad 4x^2 - 280x + 2400 = 0$$

$$\therefore \quad x^2 - 70x + 600 = 0, \ a = 1, \ b = -70, \ c = 600$$

By quadratic formula $x=10$ or $x=60$. Since 60 is an impossible solution according to the specifications in the diagram (it wouldn't fit!) $x=10$ is the only solution. The width of the strip should be 10 m.

Example 8

The time to make a 240 km trip by car is 2 hours less than by bus. The average car speed is 20 km/h more than by bus. Find the average speed of each.

One way to do the question is to do a chart where 'x' is the speed of the bus:

	distance (km)	speed (km/h)	time (h)
bus	240	x	$\dfrac{240}{x}$
car	240	$x+20$	$\dfrac{240}{x+20}$

The bus takes two hours longer than the car. This is the key to solving the problem.

$$\therefore \quad \frac{240}{x} - \frac{240}{x+20} = 2$$

$$\therefore \quad x(x+20)\left(\frac{240}{x} - \frac{240}{x+20}\right) = 2x(x+20)$$

$$\therefore \quad 240(x+20) - 240x = 2x(x+20)$$

$$\therefore \quad 2x^2 + 40x - 4800 = 0$$

$$\therefore \quad x^2 + 20x - 2400 = 0, \ a = 1, \ b = 20, \ c = -2400$$

34

By the quadratic formula $x = 40$ or $x = -60$. The negative value is rejected (speed is not negative). Therefore the average bus speed is 40 km/h and car speed is 60 km/h.

Another way to do the question is to do a chart in which 'x' represents the time in hours by bus:

	distance (km)	speed (km/h)	time (h)
bus	240	x	$\dfrac{240}{x}$
car	240	x-2	$\dfrac{240}{x-2}$

The car travels 20 km/h faster than the bus.

$\therefore \quad \dfrac{240}{x-2} - \dfrac{240}{x} = 20$

$\therefore \quad 20x^2 - 40x - 480 = 0$

$\therefore \quad x^2 - 2x - 24 = 0, \ a = 1, \ b = -2, \ c = -24,$

therefore by quadratic formula, $x = 6$ or $x = -4$ but the negative value, $x = -4$, for time is rejected so $x = 6$ only.

If $x = 6$, the speed by bus is $\dfrac{240}{6} = 40$ km/h and by car

is $\dfrac{240}{6-2} = 60$ km/h, same as above.

Example 9

The legs of a right-angled triangle measure 2 cm less and 9 cm less than the hypotenuse. Find the length of the hypotenuse.

Let the length of the hypotenuse be represented by 'x'.

$\therefore$ leg lengths in cm are $'x-2'$ and $'x-9'$

$\therefore$ $(x-2)^2 + (x-9)^2 = x^2$

$\therefore$ $x^2 - 22x + 85 = 0$, $a = 1$, $b = -22$, $c = 85$

By quadratic formula, $x = 5$ or $x = 17$.

The first figure gives negative length.

The hypotenuse is 17 cm long.

PRACTICE EXERCISE

1. Determine the nature of the roots and solve each of the following:

   a) $4x^2 = 8x - 3$ b) $5x^2 + 6x + \dfrac{9}{5} = 0$

   c) $\dfrac{7}{2-x} + \dfrac{1}{x} = 4$

2. Find two numbers whose sum is 19 and whose product is 60.

3. Find two numbers which differ by 7 and whose sum of their squares is 289.

4. A picture 2 cm by 7 cm in dimensions requires a frame in which the total area including the frame is 104 cm^2. Find the width of the frame.

5. If a bus travelled 30 km/h slower, it would take 3 hours more to make a 400 km trip. What is its speed?

CHAPTER SEVEN

Equations involving maxima and minima

Problems which require finding optimal solutions are very common in physics, engineering and business. Basically, the scientist, engineer, or business manager is asked to calculate the most effective use of a particular set of variables to give the most efficient results, i.e. maximize profits, minimize production costs, optimize temperature for chemical reactions, etc.

We are usually limited by physical conditions or limited resources of the variables such as available machine time per day or space restrictions for seating. These limitations put a **constraint equation** on the variables.

Example 1

Find two numbers which differ by 12 so that the sum of their squares is a minimum.

Define two variables, one for each number using 'let' statements and make an equation relating the two variables. Solve for one variable (it does not matter which one) in terms of the other.

Let the larger number be represented by 'x'.
Let the smaller number be represented by 'y'.

Then $x - y = 12$, hence $y = x - 12$. Let S represent the sum of their squares, then $S = x^2 + y^2$.

Substitute $y = x - 12$ to get 'S' in terms of one variable.

$\therefore \quad S = x^2 + (x-12)^2$

$\therefore \quad S = 2x^2 - 24x + 144, \quad \therefore a = 2, \ b = -24, \ c = 144$

The maximum or minimum value of a quadratic equation

is always at $x = \dfrac{-b}{2a}$

$\therefore$ the minimum sum of their squares is at

$\quad x = \dfrac{-b}{2a} = \dfrac{-(-24)}{2(2)} = 6$ and so $y = 6 - 12 = -6$.

Therefore the two numbers are -6 and 6.

Example 2

The perimeter of a rectangular fence is 240 m.
a) Find the dimensions of the fence with maximum area.
b) Find the maximum area.

a) Let the length and width in metres be represented by 'L' and 'W' respectively.

$\therefore \quad 2L + 2W = 240$

$\therefore \quad L + W = 120$

$\therefore \quad W = 120 - L$

Let the area in m^2 be represented by 'A'.

$\therefore \quad A = L(120 - L)$

$\qquad = 120L - L^2$

$\qquad = -L^2 + 120L$

$\qquad$ (which is equivalent to $y = -x^2 + 120x$,

$\qquad\qquad\qquad a = -1, \ b = 120, \ c = 0$)

$\therefore \quad L = \dfrac{-b}{2a} = \dfrac{(-120)}{2(-1)} = 60,$

$\therefore \quad W = 120 - 60 = 60$.

The dimensions for maximum area are 60 m by 60 m.

b) The maximim area is therefore $60 \times 60 = 3600 \ m^2$.

Guidelines to solving equations involving maxima and minima

1. Translate English into algebra to obtain two equations:

(i) One equation will be a combination of two variables which equals a constant. This is called the **constraint equation**. Express one variable in terms of the other. Use a labelled diagram if necessary. Remember to define the variables in a 'let' statement and state the units of the variables.

(ii) The other equation is the equation to be maximized or minimized. It is expressed in terms of the two variables above. Substitute using the constraint equation to express it in terms of one variable in descending powers, i.e. $T = ax^2 + bx + c$, which is the equation of a parabola.

2. If a>0, the parabola opens up and the value of 'T' at the vertex is a minimum.
    If a<0, the parabola opens down and the value of 'T' at the vertex is a maximum.

    The maximum or minimum value of T' is at $x = \dfrac{-b}{2a}$.

3. Make a complete English statement which answers the question for a conclusion.

Example 3

A movie is attended by 200 people when the admission price is $3. For every $0.25 increase in the admission price ten fewer people will attend. What price will maximize the revenues?

Let N represent the number of people attending.
Let C represent the cost in dollars per ticket.
Let 'x' represent the number of $0.25 increases of the admission price.

$\therefore$ number of people attending is represented by $N = 200 - 10x$
$\therefore$ cost per ticket is represented by $C = 3 + 0.25x$

Let the admissions revenue in dollars be represented by R.

$\therefore \quad R = (N)(C)$

$\qquad = (200 - 10x)(3 + 0.25x)$

$\qquad = -2.5x^2 + 20x + 600, \ a = -2.5, b = 20, c = 600$

$\therefore \quad$ for maximum revenues, $x = \dfrac{-b}{2a} = \dfrac{-(20)}{2(-2.5)} = 4.$

$\therefore \quad$ four increases of $0.25 over the $3 admission price will maximize the take at the gate. The most profitable admission price would be $3 + 4(0.25) = \$4$.

PRACTICE EXERCISE

1. Two numbers have a sum of 52. If their product is a maximum, find the two numbers.

2. A rectangular field is bounded on one side by a river and on the other three sides by 60 m of fencing. Find the dimensions of the largest possible field.

3. When a bus fare is $1.50, two thousand people ride it per day. For every $0.15 increase in the fare, ridership decreases by 50 people. What should be charged to maximize the revenues?

CHAPTER EIGHT

Absolute value equations

The absolute value of a number, stated as $|a|$, means the distance the coordinate 'a' is from zero on a number line. As you can see in the diagram the absolute value of three, and the absolute value of negative three are both 3 since the coordinates are both 3 units from zero. Therefore $|3|=|-3|=3$.

$$\overleftarrow{\quad 3\ cm\quad}\blacktriangleright\ \overleftarrow{\quad 3\ cm\quad}\longrightarrow$$

-3	0	3

Since distance is always a positive measure, absolute values are always positive, $|a|\geq 0$ and $|a|=|-a|$.

Example 1

Solve $|x| = 5$.

Graph the left side of the equation, $y = |x|$, which is the union of the parts of two equations which lie above the x-axis, $y = x$ and $y = -x$. On the same set of axes graph the right side of the equation, $y = 5$. The answer will be the x-coordinates of the points of intersection as shown in the diagram.

41

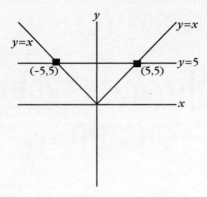

The answer is $x=5$ or $x=-5$.

How to solve an equation with an absolute value

1. Isolate an absolute value term on one side of the equation.
2. Graph all the 'V' shaped absolute value terms by graphing the parts of the positive and negative of the absolute value expression which appear above the x-axis. (Graph the term without an absolute value if there is one.)
3. The solution will be the x-coordinates of the points of intersection of these graphs.

Example 2

Solve $|x+2| = 7$.

Graph the 'V' shaped $y=|x+2|$ by graphing the parts of the graphs of the lines $y=x+2$ and $y=-x-2$ which lie above the x-axis. On the same set of axes, graph the right side of the equation, $y=7$. The answer will be the x-coordinates of the points of intersection as shown in the diagram.

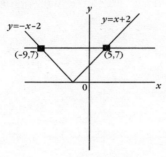

The answers are $x=-9$ and $x=7$.

Example 3

Solve $|x-3| - 2x = 0$.

Solving the equation, we find that $|x-3| = 2x$. Graph the 'V' shaped $y=|x-3|$ by graphing the parts of the graphs of the lines $y=x-3$ and $y=-x+3$ which lie above the x-axis. On the same set of axes, graph the right side of the equation, $y=2x$. The answer will be the x-coordinates of the points of intersection as shown in the diagram.

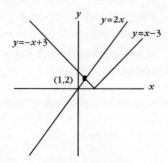

The answer is $x=1$.

Example 4

Solve $|x+1| = |2x-7|$.

Graph the 'V' shaped left side of the equation $y=|x+1|$ by graphing the parts of the graphs of $y=x+1$ and $y=-x-1$ which lie above the x-axis. On the same set of axes graph the right side of the equation, the 'V' shaped $y=|2x-7|$ by graphing the parts of the graphs of $y=2x-7$ and $y=-2x+7$ which lie above the x-axis. The answer will be the x-coordinates of the points of intersection as shown in the diagram.

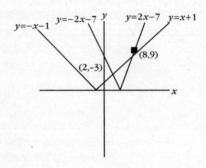

The answers are $x=2$ or $x=8$.

PRACTICE EXERCISES

Solve

a) $|2x-1| = 8$ b) $4|4x-3| = 7x$

c) $|5x-3| = |x+9|$

CHAPTER NINE

Absolute value inequalities

In the previous chapter, we solved the problem by finding what 'x' was equal to. In this section's kind of question we only want to know what relationship (greater than, less than) there is between 'x' and the value of 'x' the equality would give.

Example 1

Solve $|x| < 3$.

Graph the 'V' shaped left side of the equation, $y = |x|$, by graphing the parts of the graphs of $y = x$ and $y = -x$ which lie above the x-axis. On the same set of axes graph the right side of the equation, $y = 3$. Determine the x-coordinates of the points of intersection. Since the inequality is a 'less than' sign, the answer will be the range of the 'x' coordinates not including the boundary values in which the 'V' graph is below the graph of $y = 3$ as shown by the heavy line in the diagram.

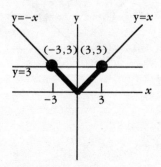

The answer is $-3 < x < 3$.

How to solve an absolute value inequality

Do the same steps as solving an **absolute value equation** except also determine which interval(s) for 'x' the absolute value 'V' graph satisfies the inequality. In other words, for what values of 'x' is the 'V' higher or lower than the graph of the right side of the equation?

Example 2

Solve $|x| \geq 5$.

Graph the 'V' shaped left side of the equation, $y = |x|$, by graphing the parts of the graphs of $y = x$ and $y = -x$ which lie above the x-axis. On the same set of axes graph the right side of the equation, $y = 5$. Determine the x-coordinates of the points of intersection. Since the inequality is a 'greater than or equal to' sign, the answer will be the range of 'x' coordinates including the boundary values in which the 'V' graph is above the graph of $y=5$ as shown by the heavy line in the diagram.

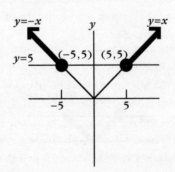

The answers are x ≤ −5 or x ≥ 5.

Example 3

Solve $|x-5| \leq 2$.

Graph the 'V' shaped left side of the equation, $y=|x-5|$, by graphing the parts of the graphs of $y=x-5$ and $y=-x+5$ which lie above the x-axis. On the same set of axes graph the right side of the equation, $y=2$. Determine the x-coordinates of the points of intersection. Since the inequality is a 'less than or equal to' sign, the answer will be the range of x-coordinates including the boundary values in which the 'V' graph is below the graph of $y=2$ as shown by the heavy line in the diagram.

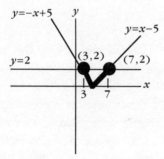

The answer is $3 \leq x \leq 7$.

Example 4

Solve $|4x-3| > 11$.

Graph the 'V' shaped left side of the equation, $y=|4x-3|$, by graphing the parts of the graphs of $y=4x-3$ and $y=-4x+3$ which lie above the x-axis. On the same set of axes graph the right side of the equation, $y=11$. Determine the x-coordinates of the points of intersection. Since the inequality is a 'greater than' sign, the answer will be the range of 'x' coordinates not including the boundary values in which the 'V' graph is above the graph of $y=11$ as shown by the heavy line in the diagram.

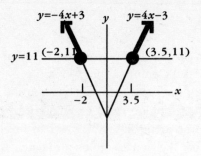

The answers are $x<-2$ or $x>3.5$.

Example 5

Solve $|x+1|>3x$.

Graph the 'V' shaped left side of the equation $y=|x+1|$, by graphing the parts of the graphs of $y=x+1$ and $y=-x-1$ which lie above the x-axis. On the same set of axes, graph the right side of the equation, $y=3x$. Determine the x-coordinates of the points of intersection. Since the inequality is a 'greater than' sign, the answer will be the range of 'x' coordinates not including the boundary values in which the 'V' graph is above the graph of $y=3x$ as shown by the heavy line in the diagram.

The answer is $x<0.5$.

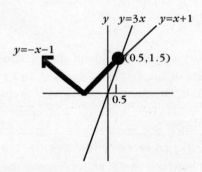

PRACTICE EXERCISES

Solve and graph each of the following:

  a) $|x-4|>3$ b) $|5x+2|\leq3$ c) $|x-2|>2x$

CHAPTER TEN

Radical equations

In mathematics, every arithmetical operation can be carried out in two directions. If we multiply, we should be able to divide to return to the original equation. But in higher level math, we find that not all operations are reversible.

For instance:

$$(-1)^2 = 1^2$$

But when we try to do the reverse by taking the square root of both sides, we have

$$-1 = 1$$

This is obviously not true. So in doing problems involving roots, we have to be careful to check any solution by substituting back into the original equation. Otherwise, it's possible to come up with invalid answers.

Example 1

Solve $\sqrt{x+4} + 2 = x$

First isolate the radical term on one side of the equation, then square both sides.

$$\therefore \quad \sqrt{x+4} = x-2$$

$$\therefore \quad (\sqrt{x+4})^2 = (x-2)^2$$

Simplify, placing all the terms in descending power order on one side of the equation leaving zero on the other side.

$$\therefore \quad x+4=x^2-4x+4$$
$$\therefore \quad x^2-5x=0$$

Solve by any method such as factoring or by quadratic formula, then check each solution in the original equation for invalid values.

$$\therefore \quad x(x-5)=0$$
$$\therefore \quad x=0 \text{ or } x=5$$

Substituting $x=0$ into the original equation we obtain

$$\sqrt{0+4}+2=0$$

i.e. $4=0$ which is impossible so $x=0$ is rejected as an answer. Substituting $x=5$ into the original equation we obtain

$$\sqrt{5+4}+2=5$$

which is a true statement, so $x=5$ is the only answer.

Steps to solving a radical equation with one radical term

1. Isolate the radical term on one side of the equation.
2. Square both sides of the equation and simplify placing all terms in descending power order on one side of the equation leaving zero on the other side.
3. Solve by factoring or quadratic formula.
4. Check each solution for invalid values by substituting into the original equation.

Example 2

Solve $\sqrt{2x-3} + \sqrt{x+2} = 3$

Seperate the radical terms on opposite sides of the equal sign (either one may be moved) then square both sides.

$$\therefore \quad \sqrt{2x-3} = 3 - \sqrt{x+2}$$
$$\therefore \quad (\sqrt{2x-3})^2 = (3 - \sqrt{x+2})^2$$
$$\therefore \quad 2x-3 = 9 - 6\sqrt{x+2} + x + 2$$

Simplify then isolate the radical term on one side of the equation so we can square both sides again.

$$\therefore \quad 6\sqrt{x+2} = 14 - x$$
$$\therefore \quad (6\sqrt{x+2})^2 = (14-x)^2$$
$$\therefore \quad 36(x+2) = 196 - 28x + x^2$$
$$\therefore \quad 36x + 72 = 196 - 28x + x^2$$
$$\therefore \quad 0 = x^2 - 64x + 124, a = 1, b = -64, c = 124$$
$$\therefore \quad x = \frac{64 \pm \sqrt{(-64)^2 - 4(1)(124)}}{2(1)}$$
$$\therefore \quad x = \frac{64 \pm \sqrt{3600}}{2}$$
$$\therefore \quad x = 2 \text{ or } x = 62.$$

Substituting $x = 2$ into the original equation gives

$$\therefore \quad \sqrt{2(2)-3} + \sqrt{2+2} = 3$$
$$\therefore \quad \sqrt{1} + \sqrt{4} = 3, \text{ which is true! We accept the answer } x = 2.$$

Substituting x= 62 into the original equation gives

$$\therefore \quad \sqrt{2(62)-3} + \sqrt{62+2} = 3$$
$$\therefore \quad \sqrt{121} + \sqrt{64} = 3,$$

which is not true so $x = 62$ is rejected as an answer.

Steps to solving a radical equation with two radical terms

1. Separate the radical terms on different sides of the equation, then square both sides.
2. Simplify and isolate the radical term on one side of the equation. Square both sides again.
3. Simplify and place all terms in descending powers on one side of the equation leaving zero on the other side. Solve by factoring or by quadratic formula.
4. Check each solution for invalid values by substituting into the original equation.

Example 3

Solve $1 + \dfrac{\sqrt{x+4}}{\sqrt{x-3}} = \dfrac{7}{\sqrt{x-3}}$

Clear fractions by multiplying both sides by the least common denominator, $\sqrt{x-3}$.

$$\therefore \quad \sqrt{x-3}\left(1 + \frac{\sqrt{x+4}}{\sqrt{x-3)}}\right) = \sqrt{x-3}\left(\frac{7}{\sqrt{x-3}}\right)$$

$$\therefore \quad \sqrt{x-3} + \sqrt{x+4} = 7$$

Separate the radicals on different sides of the equation, then square both sides.

$$\therefore \quad \sqrt{x-3} = 7 - \sqrt{x+4}$$

$$\therefore \quad \left(\sqrt{x-3}\right)^2 = \left(7 - \sqrt{x+4}\right)^2$$

$$\therefore \quad x - 3 = 49 - 14\sqrt{x+4} + x + 4$$

Isolate the radical term on one side of the equation then square both sides.

$\therefore \quad 14\sqrt{x+4} = 56,$ divide both sides by 14 to reduce the equation to lowest terms.

$\therefore \quad \sqrt{x+4} = 4$

$\therefore \quad (\sqrt{x+4})^2 = 4^2$

$\therefore \quad x+4 = 16,$ i.e. $x = 12,$

then substituting $x = 12$ into the original equation gives

$$1 + \frac{\sqrt{12+4}}{\sqrt{12-3}} = \frac{7}{\sqrt{12-3}}, \text{ i.e. } 1 + \frac{4}{3} = \frac{7}{3}$$

which is true so $x = 12$ is the solution.

PRACTICE EXERCISE

Solve for the variable in each of the following:

a) $\sqrt{x-2} + 8 = x$

b) $\sqrt{x-5} + \sqrt{3x+9} = 8$

c) $\sqrt{x+1} = \frac{3}{\sqrt{x-1}} - \sqrt{x-1}$

Quadratic inequalities

Quadratic inequalities look difficult, but their solution only requires that you set up a simple chart to find the range of answers 'x' is found to lie in.

Example 1

Solve and graph $x^2 + 2x - 15 > 0$.

Factoring the left side, we obtain $(x+5)(x-3) > 0$. Set each factor to zero and solve, $x+5=0$, so $x=-5$ and $x-3=0$ so $x=3$. Graph these numbers on a number line and number the 3 regions obtained, I, II and III. Test an easy value for 'x' in each region of the number line for each factor. Then write down the sign of the factor and the net sign of the non-zero side of the inequation in a chart. Here's an example:

	I		II		III
		-5		3	
$x+5$	$-$		$+$		$+$
$x-3$	$-$		$-$		$+$
$(x-3)(x+5)$	$+$		$-$		$+$

The 'greater than zero' part of the inequation means we are looking for the regions where the sign of $(x-3)(x+5)$ is positive. Therefore regions I and III satisfy the inequality. The solution is $x < -5$ or $x > 3$.

54

Steps to solving a quadratic inequation

1. Put all terms on one side of the inequation leaving zero on the other side.

2. Fully factor the terms of the inequation. If there are two terms or more involving fractions, make one entire fraction in factored form.

3. Set each factor to zero and solve. Graph these numbers on a number line, and number the resulting regions.

4. Test an easy number for 'x' found in each region of the number line for each factor. Then write down the sign of each factor, whether positive or negative, and then the net sign of all the factors in a chart.

5. The solution will be the numbered region(s) whose sign satisfies the inequation.

Example 2

Solve and graph $\dfrac{1}{x-2} \le \dfrac{6}{x+3}$

Place all terms on one side of the inequation.

$\therefore \quad \dfrac{1}{x-2} - \dfrac{6}{x+3} \le 0$

Make one entire fraction of the non zero side of the inequation.

$\therefore \quad \dfrac{1(x+3)-6(x-2)}{(x-2)(x+3)} \le 0$

$\therefore \quad \dfrac{-5x+15}{(x-2)(x+3)} \le 0$

Factor the top and bottom of the non zero of the inequation.

$$\therefore \quad \frac{-5(x-3)}{(x-2)(x+3)} \leq 0$$

The zeroes of each factor are -3, 2 and 3. Note the restrictions of the denominator are $x \neq 2$ and $x \neq -3$. Three numbers divide the number line into 4 regions. Test an easy value for 'x' in each region of the number line for each factor and record the sign of each factor and the net sign of the non-zero side of the inequation. We now make the following chart:

	I	II	III	IIII
	-3		2	3
$x+3$	$-$	$+$	$+$	$+$
$x-2$	$-$	$-$	$+$	$+$
$x-3$	$-$	$-$	$-$	$+$
$\dfrac{-5(x-3)}{(x-2)(x+3)}$	$+$	$-$	$+$	$-$

The 'less than or equal to zero' part of the inequation means that we are looking for the regions where the sign of

$$\frac{-5(x-3)}{(x-2)(x+3)}$$

is negative or its value equals zero. Therefore regions II and IIII satisfy the inequation. The solution is $-3 < x < 2$ or $x \geq 3$. Note the restrictions did not allow -3 and 2 to be included.

PRACTICE EXERCISE

Solve and graph each of the following:

a) $3x^2 + 10x - 8 < 0$

b) $\dfrac{2-x}{x+3} \geq 0$

c) $\dfrac{x}{x^2-4} + \dfrac{1}{x+2} \leq 0$

CHAPTER TWELVE

Powers and exponents

If you double one cent every day for 30 days i.e. after one day you have two cents, after two days you have four cents, etc., how much money would you have after 30 days? The answer is two times itself 30 times. Rather than write a two 30 times, exponent notation was invented. Thus the answer is 2^{30} which equals \$10,737,418.24. For any real number 'a' and positive integer 'm', a^m is called a **power** where 'a' is called the **base** and 'm' is called the **exponent**. $a^m = a \cdot a \cdot a \cdot \ldots a$, where factor '$a$' is multiplied '$m$' times by itself.

Example 1
Simplify each of the following:

a) $\left(x^5\right)\left(x^3\right)$ b) $\dfrac{y^5}{y^2}$ c) $\left(t^2\right)^3$ d) $\left(3m^2n\right)^3$

e) $\left(\dfrac{a^2}{b^5}\right)^2$ f) $\left(-3x^2y\right)^2\left(5x^6y^4\right)$

Solutions

a) $x^{5+3} = x^8$ b) $y^{5-2} = y^3$ c) t^6

d) $3^3\left(m^2\right)^3 n^3 = 27m^6n^3$ e) $\dfrac{\left(a^2\right)^2}{\left(b^5\right)^2} = \dfrac{a^4}{b^{10}}$

f) $\left[(-3)^2\left(x^2\right)^2 y^2\right]\left[5x^6y^4\right] = \left(9x^4y^2\right)\left(5x^6y^4\right) = 45x^{10}y^6$

Multiplication of Powers in the Same Base

$$a^m \bullet a^n = a^{m+n}$$

Division of Powers in the Same Base

$$\frac{a^m}{a^n} = a^{m-n}, \ a \neq 0$$

Power of a Power

$$(a^m)^n = a^{mn}$$

Power of a Product

$$(ab)^m = a^m b^m$$

Power of a Quotient

$$\left(\frac{a}{b}\right)^m = \frac{a^m}{b^m}, \ b \neq 0$$

Example 2

Express the following as a single power:

a) $\left(x^{2m}\right)^3\left(x^{m+2}\right)^4$

b) $\dfrac{\left(4^{3y}\right)\left(2^{y+4}\right)}{8^{y-1}}$

Solutions

a) $x^{6m}x^{4m+8} = x^{6m+(4m+8)} = x^{10m+8}$

b) Remember to express all powers in the same base.

$$\frac{\left(2^2\right)^{3y}2^{y+4}}{\left(2^3\right)^{y-1}} = \frac{2^{6y}2^{y+4}}{2^{3y-3}} = \frac{2^{7y+4}}{2^{3y-3}}$$

$$= 2^{(7y+4)-(3y-3)} = 2^{4y+7}$$

Example 3

Express as a single term: $2^x + 2^{x+3}$

Solutions

$$2^x + 2^x 2x^3 = 2^x + 8 \cdot 2^x = (1+8)2^x = 9 \cdot 2^x$$

PRACTICE EXERCISE

1. Simplify $\dfrac{\left(3c^5 d^7\right)^3 \left(4c^8 d^3\right)^2}{\left(12c^4 d^6\right)^2}$

2. Express the following as a single power

   a) $\dfrac{\left(a^{3x} b^{3y+4}\right)^4}{a^{2x} b^{5y+2}}$ b) $\dfrac{25^{3x+1} 5^{x+3}}{125^x}$

3. Express as a single term: $\dfrac{x^{10} + x^8}{x^3 + x}$

CHAPTER THIRTEEN

Zero and negative exponents

The rule for zero and negative exponents came about to keep consistency as shown in the following two examples.

Example 1

Evaluate $\dfrac{2^3}{2^3}$

Solution

$2^{3-3} = 2^0$ but $\dfrac{8}{8} = 1$ is another solution.

Since there can only be one answer, $2^0 = 1$.

Example 2

Simplify $\dfrac{x^2}{x^5}$.

Solution

$x^{2-5} = x^{-3}$ but $\dfrac{1}{\left(\dfrac{x^5}{x^2}\right)} = \dfrac{1}{x^{5-2}} = \dfrac{1}{x^3}$.

Since there can not be two answers, $x^{-3} = \dfrac{1}{x^3}$.

60

Thus the following two definitions can be made:

Zero Exponents:

$a^0 = 1$ (so long as 'a' does not equal zero)

Negative Exponents:

$$a^{-m} = \frac{1}{a^m} \quad \text{and} \quad a^m = \frac{1}{a^{-m}}$$

(so long as 'a' does not equal zero)

Example 1

Evaluate the following:

a) $\dfrac{4^5}{4^5}$

b) $\left(24x^3y^2\right)^0$

c) $\dfrac{2^3}{2^5}$

d) $\left(\dfrac{3}{4}\right)^{-2}$

e) $\dfrac{3^{-1} + 5^{-2}}{2^{-1}}$

Solutions

a) $4^{5-5} = 4^0 = 1$

b) 1

c) $2^{3-5} = 2^{-2} = \dfrac{1}{2^2} = \dfrac{1}{4}$

d) $\left(\dfrac{4}{3}\right)^2 = \dfrac{4^2}{3^2} = \dfrac{16}{9}$

e) $\dfrac{\dfrac{1}{3} + \dfrac{1}{5^2}}{\dfrac{1}{2}} = \left(\dfrac{1}{3} + \dfrac{1}{25}\right)\left(\dfrac{2}{1}\right) = \left(\dfrac{25+3}{75}\right)(2) = \left(\dfrac{28}{75}\right)(2) = \dfrac{56}{75}$

Example 2

Simplify with positive exponents only:

$$\frac{(13m^6n^{-3})(4m^{-10}n^6)}{(26m^4n^{-3})(54m^8n^{-9})^0}$$

Solution

$$\frac{(13)(4)}{26} \frac{\left[\left(m^6 m^{-10}\right)\left(n^{-3} n^6\right)\right]}{\left(m^4 n^{-3}\right)(1)} = \frac{52}{26}\left(\frac{m^{-4} n^3}{m^4 n^{-3}}\right)$$

$$= 2m^{-4-4} n^{3-(-3)}$$

$$= 2m^{-8} n^6$$

$$= \frac{2n^6}{m^8}$$

PRACTICE EXERCISE

1. Evaluate   a) $\left(\dfrac{2^3}{4^2}\right)^0$ b) $\dfrac{2^{-1}}{2^{-2} - 2^{-3}}$

2. Simplify with positive exponents only $\dfrac{(2x^{-3} y^5)^5 (xy^{-6})^4}{64x^{-4} y^{-2}}$

CHAPTER FOURTEEN

Rational exponents

The rule for rational exponents also came about to keep consistency, and this lends three more valuable concepts.

Examples

Simplify a) $(a^{\frac{1}{2}})^2$ b) $(\sqrt{a})^2$

          c) $(a^{\frac{1}{3}})^3$ d) $(\sqrt[3]{a})^3$

Solutions

  a) a b) a $\therefore a^{\frac{1}{2}} = \sqrt{a}$

  c) a d) a $\therefore a^{\frac{1}{3}} = \sqrt[3]{a}$

The following definitions can now be made:

Definitions of fraction exponents

i) $a^{\frac{1}{n}} = \sqrt[n]{a}$ (the n'th root of a,

        i.e. find a number times itself n times

        which gives the value a)

ii) $a^{\frac{m}{n}} = (\sqrt[n]{a})^m$ or $\sqrt[n]{a^m}$

iii) $\sqrt[2]{a} = \sqrt{a}$

Examples

Evaluate each of the following:

a) $16^{\frac{1}{2}}$ b) $27^{\frac{1}{3}}$ c) $(-32)^{\frac{1}{5}}$ d) $8^{\frac{-1}{3}}$

e) $16^{\frac{-3}{4}}$ f) $\left(\dfrac{4}{9}\right)^{\frac{-3}{2}}$ g) $\left(8^{\frac{2}{3}}+3^{\frac{1}{2}}\right)\left(8^{\frac{2}{3}}-3^{\frac{1}{2}}\right)$

Solutions

a) $\sqrt[2]{16}=\sqrt{16}=4$ b) $\sqrt[3]{27}=3$ c) $\sqrt[5]{-32}=-2$

d) $8^{\frac{-1}{3}}=\left(8^{\frac{1}{3}}\right)^{-1}=\left(\sqrt[3]{8}\right)^{-1}=2^{-1}=\dfrac{1}{2}$

e) $\left(16^{\frac{1}{4}}\right)^{-3}=\left(\sqrt[4]{16}\right)^{-3}=2^{-3}=\dfrac{1}{2^{3}}=\dfrac{1}{8}$

f) $\left(\dfrac{9}{4}\right)^{\frac{3}{2}}=\left[\left(\dfrac{9}{4}\right)^{\frac{1}{2}}\right]^{3}=\left(\sqrt{\dfrac{9}{4}}\right)^{3}=\left(\dfrac{\sqrt{9}}{\sqrt{4}}\right)^{3}=\left(\dfrac{3}{2}\right)^{3}=\dfrac{3^{3}}{2^{3}}=\dfrac{27}{8}$

g) $\left(8^{\frac{2}{3}}\right)^{2}-\left(3^{\frac{1}{2}}\right)^{2}=8^{\frac{4}{3}}-3=\left(\sqrt[3]{8}\right)^{4}-3=2^{4}-3=16-3=13$

Practice Exercises

Evaluate the following:

a) $(0.008)^{\frac{2}{3}}$ b) $81^{-0.25}$ c) $\left(\dfrac{-27}{125}\right)^{\frac{-4}{3}}$

d) $\left(16^{\frac{3}{4}}+7^{\frac{1}{2}}\right)\left(16^{\frac{3}{4}}-7^{\frac{1}{2}}\right)$

CHAPTER FIFTEEN

Exponential equations

The basic concept is easy: If two powers in the same base are equal, then the exponents are equal as well. This fact lets us solve many equations.

Example 1

Solve $4\left(9^{x-1}\right) = 108$

Solution

Dividing both sides by 4 gives $9^{x-1} = 27$.

Next express both sides in powers of 3

$\therefore \quad (3^2)^{x-1} = 3^3$

$\therefore \quad 3^{2x-2} = 3^3$

$\therefore \quad 2x - 2 = 3$ and so $x = 2.5$.

To test this answer, substitute $x = 2.5$ into $4\left(9^{x-1}\right)$:

$\therefore \quad 4\left(9^{2.5-1}\right) = 4\left(9^{1.5}\right)$

$= 4\left(9^{\frac{3}{2}}\right)$

$= 4\left(\sqrt{9}\right)^3$

$= 4(3)^3$

$= 108$, which checks with the question!

Example 2

Solve $6^x = \dfrac{1}{36}$.

Solution

$\therefore \quad 6^x = \dfrac{1}{6^2}$

$\therefore \quad 6^x = 6^{-2}$

$\therefore \quad x = -2$

Example 3

Solve $5^{2x} - 30 \cdot 5^x + 125 = 0$

Solution

$(5^x)^2 - 30 \cdot 5^x + 125 = 0$, substitute $y = 5^x$.

$\therefore \quad y^2 - 30y + 125 = 0$

$\therefore \quad (y-5)(y-25) = 0$

$\therefore \quad y = 5$ or $y = 25$, then put back 'x'

$\therefore \quad 5^x = 5$ or $5^x = 25$

$\therefore \quad x = 1$ or $x = 2$

Example 4

Solve $4^x + 4^{x+1} = 40$

Solution

$\therefore \quad 4^x + 4 \cdot 4^x = 40$, then common factor 4^x.

$\therefore \quad (1+4)4^x = 40$

$\therefore \quad 5 \cdot 4^x = 40$, divide both sides by 5.

$\therefore \quad 4^x = 8$

$\therefore \quad (2^2)^x = 2^3$

$\therefore \quad 2^{2x} = 2^3$

$\therefore \quad 2x = 3$ and so $x = 1.5$.

Example 5

Solve $3^{x-y} = 9$ and $27^y = 3^{x+2}$.

Solution

$3^{x-y} = 3^2$ produces the first equation in x and y which is

$x - y = 2$. Also $\left(3^3\right)^y = 3^{x+2}$, therefore $3^{3y} = 3^{x+2}$,

produces the second equation which is $3y = x + 2$.

Therefore by elimination we find $x = 4$ and $y = 2$.

PRACTICE EXERCISE

Solve for all variables:

a) $2\left(5^{2x-9}\right) = 250$

b) $3^x + 3^{x+2} = 270$

c) $2^{2x} - 5 \cdot 2^x + 4 = 0$

d) $5^{x+y} = 25$ and $125^x = 5^{y-10}$.

CHAPTER SIXTEEN

Graphs of exponential functions

In astronomy, physics, biology and accounting, graphs of exponential functions can be used to describe all sorts of events – from rockets taking off to the way interest compounds over time. To understand these concepts, we must first understand the basics of graphing exponential functions.

Example 1

a) Sketch $y=0^x$ and $y=1^x$.

b) Describe the graph of each function.

Solution

For $y=0^x$, $x>0$ the graph is the positive x-axis. For $y=1^x$, the equation is equivalent to $y=1$ so the graph is a horizontal line with y-intercept 1.

Example 2

a) Sketch $y=2^x$, $y=3^x$ and $y=10^x$.

b) What is the domain (range of values for 'x' in the graph) and range (range of values for 'y' in the graph) of these graphs?

c) Which point do these graphs share in common?

d) Are these graphs increasing or decreasing?

e) As the value of the base increases, how do the graphs change?

Solutions

a)

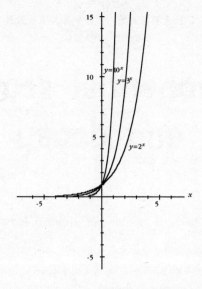

b) The domain is all the real numbers and the range is $y > 0$ for all of them.

c) $(0,1)$ because a zero exponent gives one always for a non-zero base.

d) Increasing.

e) The rise of the graphs becomes steeper.

PRACTICE EXERCISE

1. Sketch $y = 2^{-x}$, $y = 3^{-x}$ and $y = 10^{-x}$. (Hint: the graph of $y = f(-x)$ is symmetric to the graph of $y = f(x)$ in the y-axis, use this fact to quickly sketch all three). Do the questions of Example #2 b, c, d, and e.

2. Generalize the answers to the questions of example #2 b, c, d and e for $y = a^x, a > 0$.

3. Generalize the answers to the questions of #2 b, c, d, and e for $y = a^{-x}, a > 0$.

CHAPTER SEVENTEEN

Exponential growth and decay

Example 1

A certain bacteria doubles in population by dividing every 20 minutes.

a) If there are 300 bacteria in a colony at the start, how many will there be after one hour?

b) How long will it take to have a population of 1 000 000 bacteria?

Solutions

a) Let 't' be the time in minutes and $N(t)$ be the number of bacteria after time 't' has elapsed. Then the following is a chart of the number of bacteria every 20 minutes:

t	$N(t)$
0	300
20	$300 \times 2^{\frac{20}{20}} = 600$
40	$300 \times 2^{\frac{20}{20}} = 1200$
60	$300 \times 2^{\frac{20}{20}} = 2400$
⋮	⋮
t	$300 \times 2^{\frac{t}{20}}$

70

Therefore after 't' minutes the number of bacteria,

$N(t)$, is $300 \times 2^{\frac{t}{20}}$. As seen in the chart, when $t = 60$ minutes,

$$\therefore \quad N(60) = 300 \cdot 2^{\frac{60}{20}}$$
$$= 300 \cdot 2^3$$
$$= 2400$$

There will be 2400 bacteria after one hour.

The following is a simple rule for exponential growth by doubling:

Formula for Doubling

$$N(t) = c \cdot 2^{\frac{t}{d}}$$

where $N(t)$ represents the number after
time 't', 'c' represents the starting population
and 'd' represents the doubling time.

b) We're looking for the time when the population of bacteria
will be one million. Therefore $N(t) = 1\ 000\ 000$. When $c = 300$
and $d = 20$ we have

$$\therefore \quad 1\ 000\ 000 = 300 \cdot 2^{\frac{t}{20}}$$

$$\therefore \quad 2^{\frac{t}{20}} = 3333.3, \quad \text{let } x = \frac{t}{20}.$$

$$\therefore \quad 2^x = 3333.3, \quad \text{then solve for } x \text{ by trial and error, } \therefore \ x = 11.7$$

$$\therefore \quad \frac{t}{20} = 11.7$$

$$\therefore \quad t = 234 \text{ minutes, therefore it will take 3.9 hours to have a}$$
population of 1 000 000 bacteria.

Example 2

Another kind of bacteria doubles in population every three hours. If there was 10 000 bacteria after 6 hours, how many bacteria were there at the start?

Solution

At the end of 6 hours there are 10 000 bacteria, therefore $N(6) = 10\ 000$ where $t=6$, and the doubling time is 3 hours, therefore $d=3$.

$$\therefore \quad 10\ 000 = c \cdot 2^{\frac{2}{3}}$$

$$\therefore \quad C = 10\ 000 \div \left(\sqrt[3]{2}\right)^2 \approx 6299.6 = 6300$$

Example 3

Carbon 14 decays such that half of it is left in 5800 years. Find the amount of 48g of carbon 14 which will remain in 23 200 years.

Solution

Let 't' be the time in years passed and $m(t)$ be the mass in grams left at the end. Then the following is a chart of the mass of carbon remaining every 5800 years.

t	m(t)
0	48
5800	$48 \times \left(\frac{1}{2}\right)^{\frac{5800}{5800}} = 24$
11600	$48 \times \left(\frac{1}{2}\right)^{\frac{11600}{5800}} = 12$
17400	$48 \times \left(\frac{1}{2}\right)^{\frac{17400}{5800}} = 6$
23200	$48 \times \left(\frac{1}{2}\right)^{\frac{23200}{5800}} = 3$
t	$48 \times \left(\frac{1}{2}\right)^{\frac{t}{5800}}$

Therefore after 't' years the amount in the grams of carbon 14

remaining is $m(t) = 48\left(\dfrac{1}{2}\right)^{\frac{t}{5800}} = 48(2)^{\frac{-t}{5800}}$. As seen in the chart

when $t = 23\ 200$ years, the amount of carbon remaining is

$$\therefore \quad m(23\ 200) = 48 \cdot 2^{\frac{-23\ 200}{5800}}$$

$$= 48 \cdot 2^{-4}$$

$$= \frac{48}{2^4}$$

$$= 3, \quad \text{therefore there are 3 grams left.}$$

The following is the rule for exponential decay by halving.

Formula for half-life

$$m(t) = c \cdot \left(\frac{1}{2}\right)^{\frac{t}{b}} = c \cdot 2^{\frac{-t}{b}},$$

where m(t) represents the mass or amount at the end of time, t, 'c' represents the amount at the start and 'b' represents the time it takes for half the amount at the start to decay (i.e. the half-life).

Example 4

If $\dfrac{1}{32}$ of an unknown material decays after 30 hours, find it's **half - life**.

Solution

At the start of decay the amount of material is 'c', however at the end the amount is '$\dfrac{1}{32}c$'.

$$\therefore \quad \frac{1}{32}c = c \cdot 2^{\frac{-30}{h}}, \text{ we divide both sides by } 'c'.$$

$$\therefore \quad \frac{1}{32} = 2^{\frac{-30}{h}}$$

$$\therefore \quad \frac{1}{2^5} = 2^{\frac{-30}{h}}$$

$$\therefore \quad 2^{-5} = 2^{\frac{-30}{h}}$$

$$\therefore \quad -5 = \frac{-30}{h}$$

$$\therefore \quad h = 6, \text{ therefore the } \textbf{half - life} \text{ is 6 hours.}$$

Example 5

Find the amount you would have in the bank if your account started with one cent, and the bank paid 7% interest, compounded annually, for 200 years.

Solution

Let 'A' represent the value of one cent at 7% compounded annually after 'n' payment periods. Then the following is a chart of the bank balance at the end of every year:

n	A
1	$.01(1.07)$
2	$.01(1.07)(1.07) = .01(1.07)^2$
3	$.01(1.07)^2(1.07) = .01(1.07)^3$
⋮	⋮
n	$.01(1.07)^n$

Therefore the value of one cent at 7% compounded annually for 'n' years, A, is $.01(1.07)^n$. The value of one cent at 7% compounded annually for 200 years is $.01(1.07)^{200} = \$7\,529.32$. The moral of course, is that every penny counts!

Formula for compound interest

$A = P(1+i)^n$ where 'A' represents the **amount at the end**,
P is the **principal** (the amount invested at the start),
'i' is the **interest per payment period** and
'n' is the **number of payment periods**.

Example 6

How long does it take to double your money at 7% compounded annually?

Solution

Let the amount at the start be 'c', then the amount at the end is '$2c$'. Given $i = 0.07$ we have

$$\therefore \quad 2c = c \cdot (1.07)^n, \text{ divide both sides by '} c\text{'}$$

$$\therefore \quad (1.07)^n = 2, \text{ then find '} n \text{' by trying on a calculator}$$

$$n = 1, 2, 3, \text{ etc.}$$

We see that $n = 10$ is closest to making a true statement out of $\therefore \ (1.07)^n = 2$. Therefore it takes 10 years at this rate to double your money.

Example 7

Suppose a car which costs $50 000 depreciates in value at 15% per year. How much is it worth in 5 years?

Solution

If 15 % of the car value is lost every year then 85 % is left after each year, therefore $i = -0.15$.

Substitute $i = -0.15$, $n = 5$, $P = 50\ 000$.

$$\therefore \quad A = 50\ 000 \cdot (0.85)^5$$

$\therefore \quad A = \$22\ 185.27$, therefore the car is worth $\$22\ 185.27$
in five years.

PRACTICE EXERCISE

For this chapter, use your calculator for a trial-and-error estimate of the answer. In the next section, we'll show you how to find an exact answer using logarithims

1. A colony of 200 bacteria grows to 4500 bacteria in 10 hours. What is the doubling period?

2. A sample of a radiactive substance decays to 15% of its original mass in 75 years. What is its half-life?

3. How long does it take $1000 to amount to $1500 if invested at 9% per annum compounded quarterly?

Logarithmic functions

Example 1

Here is an exercise to learn the relationship of the **logarithmic function** to the **exponential function**:

a) Sketch, $y = 2^x$, i.e. $f(x) = 2^x$.
b) Sketch $y = f^{-1}(x)$. Since $(x,y) \xrightarrow{f^{-1}} (y,x)$, the graph $y = f^{-1}(x)$ is the mirror image of the graph of $y = f(x)$ in the line $y = x$, you can reverse the table of values for $y = f(x)$, sketch, then check to see if the two graphs are symmetric.
c) What is the domain and range of $y = f^{-1}(x)$?

Solutions

a) and b)

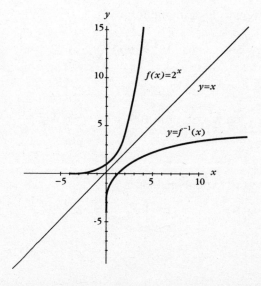

c) The domain is x > 0 and the range is all real numbers. For $y = f^{-1}(x)$, $x = 2^y$. Solving for 'y' is the standard way to express an equation. To solve for a variable in the exponent position cannot be done using algebra so the concept called a 'logarithm' had to be invented.

Definition of a Logarithm

We let $x = a^y$ mean $y = \log_a x$, which reads 'y equals log x base 'a' where '**log**' always equals the exponent 'y'.
We also let '$y = \log x$' mean '$y = \log_{10} x$' always, i.e. if the base is not stated then it is understood to mean base 10.

This definition allows us to state the equation of the inverse of the exponential function.

In our example $y = \log_2 x$ is the equation of the inverse of $y = 2^x$, i.e. $f^{-1}(x) = \log_2 x$.

Example 2

Convert to logarithmic form

a) $x = 5^y$ b) $10^3 = 1000$ c) $2^{-3} = \dfrac{1}{8}$

Solutions

a) $y = \log_5 x$ b) $\log 1000 = 3$ c) $\log_2 \dfrac{1}{8} = -3$

Example 3

Convert to exponential form

a) $\log_3 9 = 2$ b) $\log_5 \left(\dfrac{1}{25} \right) = -2.$

78

Solutions

a) $3^2 = 9$ b) $5^{-2} = \dfrac{1}{25}$

Example 4

Evaluate

a) $\log_2 64$

b) $\log 0.001$

c) $\log_8 1$

d) $\log_{-2}(-8)$

Solutions

a) We let $x = \log_2 64$, then this means

   $2^x = 64, \ \therefore 2^x = 2^6 \therefore x = 6$

b) We let $x = \log_{10} 0.001$, then this means

   $10^x = 0.001 \ \therefore 10^x = \dfrac{1}{1000}$

   $\therefore 10^x = 10^{-3}$

   $\therefore x = -3.$

c) We let $x = \log_8 1$, then this means

   $8^x = 1 \therefore 8^x = 8^0 \therefore x = 0$

d) We let $x = \log_{-2}(-8)$, then this means

   $(-2)^x = -8 \therefore (-2)^x = (-2)^3 \therefore x = 3$

Example 5

Evaluate

a) $\log x = 6$

b) $\log_x 25 = 2$

c) $\log_{\frac{1}{2}} 2 = x$

d) $\log_{27} x = \dfrac{4}{3}$

Solutions

a) This means $\log_{10} x = 6 \therefore x = 10^6 = 1\,000\,000$

b) This means $x^2 = 25 \therefore x = \pm 5$

c) This means $\left(\dfrac{1}{2}\right)^x = 2 \therefore \left(2^{-1}\right)^x = 2 \therefore 2^{-x} = 2^1$

$\therefore -x = 1 \therefore x = -1$

d) This means $x = 27^{\frac{4}{3}} \therefore x = \left(\sqrt[3]{27}\right)^4 \therefore x = 3^4 \therefore x = 81$

PRACTICE EXERCISE

1. Evaluate   a) $\log 0.0001$ b) $\log_9 \dfrac{1}{27}$ c) $\dfrac{\log_3 9}{\log_3 27}$

2. Solve   a) $\log_x 8 = \dfrac{3}{4}$ b) $\log_8 x = \dfrac{-2}{3}$

CHAPTER NINETEEN

The laws of logarithms

Remember a 'log' means an 'exponent', therefore the laws below are like the laws of exponents.

The Laws of Logarithms

- $\log_a MN = \log_a M + \log_a N$ **(multiplying rule)**

- $\log_a \dfrac{M}{N} = \log_a M - \log_a N$ **(dividing rule)**

- $\log_a M^n = n\log_a M$ **(power rule)**

More Properties of Logarithms

- $\log_a(a^n) = a^{(\log_a n)} = n$ **(rule for inverses)**

- $\log_a \dfrac{1}{M} = -\log_a M$ **(rule for reciprocals)**

- $\log_a \sqrt[n]{M} = \dfrac{1}{n}\log_a M$ **(rule for roots)**

- $\log_a b = \dfrac{\log_y b}{\log_y a}$ **(log conversion formula where 'y' is the desired base)**

Example 1

Evaluate $\log 40 + \log 2.5$.

Solution

Use the **multiplying rule**, $\log[(40)(2.5)] = \log_{10} 100 = 2$.

Example 2

Evaluate $\log_3 54 - \dfrac{1}{4}\log_3 16$.

Solution

$$\log_3 54 - \log_3 16^{\frac{1}{4}} = \log_3 54 - \log_3 2,$$
$$= \log_3 \frac{54}{2}$$
$$= \log_3 27$$
$$= 3$$

Example 3

Evaluate $\log_2 \sqrt[5]{16}$.

Solution

Use the **rule for roots** $\dfrac{1}{5}\log_2 16 = \left(\dfrac{1}{5}\right)(4) = \dfrac{4}{5}$.

Example 4

Evaluate $25^{(\log_5 3)}$.

Solution

$$\left(5^2\right)^{\log_5 3} = 5^{2\log_5 3}$$
$$= 5^{\left(\log_5 3^2\right)} \text{ (power rule)}$$
$$= 5^{\left(\log_5 9\right)}$$
$$= 9 \text{ (rule for inverses)}$$

Example 5

Evaluate $2^{\left[(\log_2 5)+1\right]}$

Solution

$$2^{\log_2 5} \cdot 2^1 = (5)(2) = 10$$

Example 6

Evaluate $\log_3 50$ to two decimal places.

Solution

Using the log conversion formula, $\dfrac{\log 50}{\log 3}$,

then on your calculator, press log 50 divided by log 3 to get 3.56.

Example 7

Express the following as a single term using the laws of logarithms:

$$\frac{1}{2}\log 2 + \frac{1}{2}\log x + \frac{1}{2}\log y - \frac{5}{2}\log z$$

Solution

$$\log 2^{\frac{1}{2}} + \log x^{\frac{1}{2}} + \log y^{\frac{1}{2}} - \log z^{\frac{5}{2}}$$

$$= \log \sqrt{2} + \log \sqrt{x} + \log \sqrt{y} - \log\left(\sqrt{z^5}\right)$$

$$= \log \sqrt{2xy} - \log\left(\sqrt{z^5}\right) \quad \textbf{(multiplying rule)}$$

$$= \log \sqrt{\frac{2xy}{z^5}} \quad \textbf{(dividing rule)}$$

PRACTICE EXERCISE

1. Evaluate   a) $\log 450 - \log 9 + \log 2$ b) $\dfrac{1}{3}\log 8 + \log 5$

2. Evaluate $\log_4 1000$ to two decimal places.

3. Express the following as a single term using the laws of logarithms:

$$\frac{3}{2}\log_3 x - \frac{\log_3 y}{2} - \frac{7\log_3 z}{2}.$$

CHAPTER TWENTY

Logarithmic equations

Solving for the variable in a logarithmic equation requires the removal of the word 'log' by converting from the logarithmic form of the equation to the exponential form.

Example 1

Solve $\log_7(x+4) + \log_7(x-2) = 1$.

Solution

$$\therefore \quad \log_7(x+4)(x-2) = 1$$
$$\therefore \quad (x+4)(x-2) = 7^1$$
$$\therefore \quad x^2 + 2x - 8 = 7$$
$$\therefore \quad x^2 + 2x - 15 = 0$$
$$\therefore \quad (x+5)(x-3) = 0$$
$$\therefore \quad x = -5 \text{ or } x = 3.$$

Recall for $y = \log x$, $x > 0$ always. $x = -5$ is rejected because when substituted into the original equation we get logs of negative numbers. $x = 3$ checks by substitution into the original equation, therefore $x = 3$ is the only solution.

Example 2

Solve $\log x^{\log x} = 1$.

Solution

$\therefore \quad (\log x)(\log x) = 1$ (Remember, this is the **power rule**)

$\therefore \quad (\log x)^2 = 1$

$\therefore \quad \log x = \pm\sqrt{1}$

$\therefore \quad \log x = \pm 1$

$\therefore \quad \log x = 1$ or $\log x = -1$

$\therefore \quad \log_{10} x = 1$ or $\log_{10} x = -1$

$\therefore \quad x = 10$ or $x = 10^{-1} = 0.1$

Example 3

Solve $(\log x)^2 = 4 - 3\log x$.

Solution

$\therefore \quad (\log x)^2 + 3\log x - 4 = 0$

If we let $y = \log x$, then by substituting we get $y^2 + 3y - 4 = 0$.

$\therefore \quad (y+4)(y-1) = 0$

$\therefore \quad y = 4$ or $y = 1$

$\therefore \quad \log x = -4$ or $\log x = 1$

$\therefore \quad x = 10^{-4} = 0.0001$ or $x = 10$.

Example 4

Solve $\log_2 x - \log_{32} x = 64$.

Solution

Use the log conversion formula to obtain $\dfrac{\log x}{\log 2} - \dfrac{\log x}{\log 32} = 64$.

Next clear fractions by multiplying by the least common denominator to obtain:

$\therefore \quad (\log 2)(\log 32)(\dfrac{\log x}{\log 2}) - (\log 2)(\log 32)(\dfrac{\log x}{\log 32})$

$\qquad = 64(\log 2)(\log 32)$

$\therefore \quad (\log 32)(\log x) - (\log 2)(\log x) = 64(\log 2)(\log 32)$

$\therefore \quad (\log 2^5)(\log x) - (\log 2)(\log x) = 64(\log 2)(\log 2^5)$

$\therefore \quad 5(\log 2)(\log x) - (\log 2)(\log x) = 320(\log 2)(\log 2)$

$$\therefore \quad 4(\log 2)(\log x) = 320(\log 2)^2$$

$$\therefore \quad 4(\log 2)(\log x) - 320(\log 2)^2 = 0$$

$$\therefore \quad 4\log 2[\log x - 80\log 2] = 0$$

$$\therefore \quad \log x - 80\log 2 = 0$$

$$\therefore \quad \log x - \log 2^{80} = 0$$

$$\therefore \quad \log \frac{x}{2^{80}} = 0$$

$$\therefore \quad \frac{x}{2^{80}} = 10^0$$

$$\therefore \quad x = 2^{80}$$

Example 5

Solve $\log_2 \log_3 \log_4 x = 0$.

Solution

$$\therefore \quad \log_2\left(\log_3\left(\log_4 x\right)\right) = 0$$

$$\therefore \quad \log_3\left(\log_4 x\right) = 2^0$$

$$\therefore \quad \log_3\left(\log_4 x\right) = 1$$

$$\therefore \quad \log_4 x = 3^1$$

$$\therefore \quad x = 4^3, \text{ therefore } x = 64.$$

PRACTICE EXERCISE

Solve each of the following

a) $\dfrac{1}{5 - \log x} + \dfrac{2}{1 + \log x} = 1$

b) $\log_9\left(x + 5\right) + \log_9\left(x - 3\right) = 1$

c) $x^{\log_8 x} = 8$

d) $\left(\log_4 x\right)^2 = \log_4 x + 6$

e) $2(\log_4 x) + 2(\log_x 4) = 5$

f) $\log \log \log \, x = 0$

CHAPTER TWENTY-ONE

Applications of logarithms

Logarithms and senior algebra have many applications in the sciences, engineering and accounting. In this chapter, we'll look at a few of them.

GROWTH AND DECAY

Example 1

If there were 100 000 bacteria in a colony at the end of two days and 150 000 at the end of three days find:

a) the doubling period

b) in how many days will there be 1 000 000 bacteria.

Solution

a) $N(t) = c \cdot 2^{\frac{t}{d}}$, at $c = 100\ 000$, $t = 3 - 2 = 1$ day, $N(1) = 150\ 000$,

$\therefore$ $150\ 000 = 100\ 000 \cdot 2^{\frac{1}{d}}$

$\therefore$ $2^{\frac{1}{d}} = 1.5$

$\therefore$ $\log 2^{\frac{1}{d}} = \log 1.5$

> We take logs on both sides of the equal sign.

$\therefore$ $\frac{1}{d} \log 2 = \log 1.5$

$\therefore$ $\frac{\log 2}{d} = \frac{\log 1.5}{1}$

$\therefore$ $\log 1.5 \cdot d = \log 2$

$\therefore$ $d = \frac{\log 2}{\log 1.5}$, therefore using a calculator, $d = 1.7\ days$.

b) $d = 1.7$ days, $c = 100\ 000$, $N(t) = 1\ 000\ 000$,

$\therefore\quad 1000000 = 100000 \cdot 2^{\frac{t}{1.7}}$

$\therefore\quad 2^{\frac{t}{1.7}} = 10$

$\therefore\quad \log 2^{\frac{t}{1.7}} = \log 10$

$\therefore\quad \dfrac{t}{1.7} \log 2 = \log_{10} 10$

$\therefore\quad \dfrac{t \log 2}{1.7} = 1$

$\therefore\quad t = \dfrac{1.7}{\log 2} = 5.7$ days

Example 2

Find the age of a mammoth whose bones have lost one tenth of their original carbon 14 mass. The half-life of carbon 14 is 5800 years.

Solution

$$m(t) = c \cdot 2^{\frac{-t}{b}}, \text{ at } b = 5800 \text{ years}, m(t) = \frac{9c}{10}$$

(The amount remaining is nine tenths of the starting amount c.)

$\therefore\quad m(t) = 0.9c.$

$0.9c = c \cdot 2^{\frac{-t}{5800}}$

$\therefore\quad 2^{\frac{-t}{5800}} = 0.9$

$\therefore\quad \log 2^{\frac{-t}{5800}} = \log 0.9$

$\therefore\quad \dfrac{-t}{5800} \log 2 = \log 0.9$

$\therefore\quad \dfrac{-t \log 2}{5800} = \log 0.9$

$\therefore\quad -t \log 2 = -265.4$

$\therefore\quad t = \dfrac{-265.4}{\log 2}$

$\therefore\quad t = 882 \text{ years}$

COMPOUND INTEREST

Example 3

How long does it take $1000 to amount to $1500 if invested at 9% per year compounded quarterly?

Solution

$P = \$1000$, $A = \$1500$, $i = 9\%$ divided into 4 payments is

$\dfrac{.09}{4} = 0.0225\%$ per payment.

$\therefore \quad 1500 = 1000 \cdot (1 + 0.0225)^n$

$\therefore \quad (1.0225)^n = 1.5$

$\therefore \quad \log 1.0225^n = \log 1.5$

$\therefore \quad n \log 1.0225 = \log 1.5$

$\therefore \quad n = \dfrac{\log 1.5}{\log 1.0225}$

$\therefore \quad n = 18.2$

Therefore this amount occures in the 19th payment period,

so it takes about $\dfrac{19}{4} = 4.75$ years.

EARTHQUAKES

On the Richter Scale, an earthquake which measures 'n' units more than another earthquake means that earthquake is 10^n times as strong. We let the magnitude of an earthquake be

$m = \log\left(\dfrac{I}{S}\right)$ where I = intensity of the earthquake, S = intensity of a standard earthquake.

$$\therefore \quad m_2 - m_1 = \log\left(\dfrac{I_2}{S}\right) - \log\left(\dfrac{I_1}{S}\right)$$

$$= \log\left[\dfrac{\dfrac{I_2}{S}}{\dfrac{I_1}{S}}\right]$$

$$= \log\left[\dfrac{I_2}{I_1}\right]$$

We now can compare earthquake intensities:

Application of logarithms to earthquake intensity

To compare two earthquake intensities of magnitudes m_1 and m_2, solve for $\dfrac{I_2}{I_1}$ where $m_2 - m_1 = \log\dfrac{I_2}{I_1}$.

Example 4

Compare the intensity of an earthquake of magnitude 8.5 on the Richter Scale to one with magnitude 6.

Solution

Let $m_1 = 6$ and $m_2 = 8.5$, therefore $8.5 - 6 = \log\dfrac{I_2}{I_1}$.

We let $x = \dfrac{I_2}{I_1}$.

$\therefore \quad \log x = 2.5$

$\therefore \quad x = 10^{2.5}$

$\therefore \quad x = 316$

Therefore the first earthquake is 316 times as strong.

Example 5

An earthquake was four times as strong as another which measured 8.3 on the Richter Scale. What was its magnitude?

Solution

Let $m_1 = 8.3$ and $\dfrac{I_2}{I_1} = 4$.

$\therefore m_2 - 8.3 = \log 4$

$\therefore m_2 = 8.3 + \log 4$

$\therefore m_2 = 8.3 + 0.6$

$\therefore m_2 = 8.9$

SOUND INTENSITY

Zero decibels (0 dB) is defined as the faintest sound most people can here. On the decibel scale for every 10 dB more, a sound measures ten times as loud. We let the magnitude of a sound in dB, $m = 10\log L$ where L equals the sound intensity compared to 0 dB. We now can compare sound intensities.

Application of logarithms to sound intensity

To compare the intensity of two sounds of magnitude m_1 and m_2 in dB, solve for $\dfrac{L_2}{L_1}$, where:

$$m_2 - m_1 = 10\log\frac{L_2}{L_1}$$

Example 6

Compare the intensity of loud music (120 dB) which can cause permanent hearing loss to ordinary talking (50 dB).

Solution

$m_1 = 50\ dB$ and $m_2 = 120\ dB$

$\therefore\quad 120 - 50 = 10\log\dfrac{L_2}{L_1}$. Let $x = \dfrac{L_2}{L_1}$,

$\therefore\quad \log x = 7$

$\therefore\quad x = 10^7$

Therefore loud music is ten million times louder than ordinary talking.

STAR BRIGHTNESS

A zero magnitude star is defined as the faintest star most people can see. The magnitude of a star, $m = -2.5\log\frac{b}{b_0}$ where 'b' is the brightness of the star and 'b_0' is the brightness of a star with magnitude zero. We now can compare the brightness of stars.

Application of Logarithms to Star Brightness

To compare the brightness of two stars of magnitudes m_1 and m_2, solve for $\dfrac{b_2}{b_1}$ where $m_2 - m_1 = -2.5\log\dfrac{b_2}{b_1}$.

Example 7

How many times as bright as Venus (magnitude -4.4) is the full moon (magnitude -12.7)?

Solution

$m_1 = -4.4$ and $m_2 = -12.7$

$\therefore \quad -12.7 - (-4.4) = -2.5\log\dfrac{b_2}{b_1}$, let $x = \dfrac{b_2}{b_1}$

$\therefore \quad -2.5\log x = -8.3$

$\therefore \quad \log x = 3.32$

$\therefore \quad x = 10^{3.32}$

$\therefore \quad x = 2089$

Therefore the full moon is 2089 times as bright as Venus.

PRACTICE EXERCISE

1. A hive of bees that started with a population of 2000 grew to 6000 in 17.4 months. What is the doubling period of the bee population.

2. The half-life of radium is 1620 years. If there were 80 mg at the start, after how many years is only 30 mg left?

3. If the population of a colony of bacteria doubles every 20 minutes, how long would it take the population to triple?

4. How long does it take money to double at 7% interest compounded semi-annually?

5. An earthquake which measured 8.2 on the Richter scale was 150 times as strong as another earthquake. What was the magnitude of the other earthquake?

6. Compare the intensity of a magnitude 7.1 earthquake to a magnitude 4.4 earthquake.

7. The sound of a 140 dB jet engine is the threshold of pain. A space shuttle launch measures 180 dB. How many more times as loud is the space shuttle launch?

8. How many times less bright is the North Star, Polaris, (magnitude 1.99) than the brightest star, Sirius, (magnitude −1.46)?

Sample exam in algebra

1. Factor fully each of the following:

a) $x^2 - 2xy - 3x + 6y$

b) $2x^2 + 6x - 36$

c) $x^4 - 34x^2y^2 + 225y^4$

d) $64x^2 - 48x + 9$

e) $16x^3 - 26x^2 + 9x$

f) $x^2 - 25y^2 + 20y - 4$

g) $64 - \dfrac{9x^2}{4}$

h) $\dfrac{x^3}{8} - 1$

i) $343x^3 + 8y^3$

j) $x^3 - 5x^2 + 2x + 8$

2. Divide $(3x^3 - 4x^2 - 13x - 1) \div (3x + 2)$

3. Find the value of k' so that $(5x^3 + kx^2 + 7x - 2)$ has $(x + 1)$ as a factor.

4. Solve each of the following.

a) $8x^2 - 3x - 5 = 0$

b) $\dfrac{x^2}{2} + x + 3 = 0$

c) $6x^3 - 25x^2 + 3x + 4 = 0$

d) $|x - 1| = 2x - 4$

e) $|3x - 1| < 4$

f) $|6x + 5| \geq 2$

g) $x^2 - 2x - 3 > 0$

h) $\dfrac{2}{x - 3} \leq \dfrac{3}{x + 5}$

i) $\sqrt{2x + 3} - \sqrt{5x + 1} + 1 = 0$

5. Express in the form $y = a(x - p)^2 + q$ by completing the square for: $y = 3x^2 - 18x + 25$.

6. A farmer builds a rectangular fence with two equal holding areas as shown against a barn. If there is 600 m of fenching available, what are the dimensions for maximum total area?

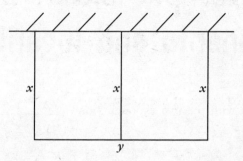

7. A rectangular painting is equal in area to the uniform strip of frame around it. If the frame measures 30 cm by 40 cm, what is the width of the strip?

8. A bike can make a 400 km ride four hours faster if its speed increases by 5 km/h. What is the speed of the bike?

Sample exam on exponents and logarithms

1. Simplify with positive exponents only: $\dfrac{(2x^{-2}y^3)^4(3x^5y^{-8})^3}{(6x^{-3}y^2)^2(5x^4y^{-2})^0}$

2. Simplify:

   a) $(4^{-1}+2^{-1})^{-1}$ b) $\left(\dfrac{49}{16}\right)^{\frac{-3}{2}}$ c) $\left(27^{\frac{2}{3}}+5^{\frac{1}{2}}\right)\left(27^{\frac{2}{3}}-5^{\frac{1}{2}}\right)$

3. Expresss as a single power: $\dfrac{\left(27^{x+5}\right)\left(3^{2-x}\right)}{81^{2x-3}}$

4. Solve for all variables:

   a) $3(6^{3x-12})=648$ b) $5^x+5^{x+2}=16250$

   c) $2^{2x+y}=16$ and $8^x=4^{y+3}$ (simultaneous equations)

5. Evaluate:

   a) $\log_4 8$ b) $\log_3\left(\dfrac{1}{27}\right)$ c) $\log_{25}125$

   d) $81^{(\log_9 5)}$

6. Solve:

   a) $\log_x 343=3$ b) $\log_8 x=\dfrac{2}{3}$

   c) $\log_6(x+3)+\log_6(x-2)=1$

   d) $\log^2 x+\log x-6=0$ g) $x^{\log x}=10000$

7. Express as a single term using the laws of logarithms:

$$\frac{2}{3}\log\left(a^2\right) - 5\log\left(b^{\frac{-1}{2}}\right) + \log\left(\frac{1}{c}\right)$$

8. If there were 7500 bacteria at the start and 20 000 one hour later

   a) what is the doubling time?

   b) in how many hours will there be 60 000?

9. The half-life of a certain element is 16 days. How long will it take 60 mg of the substance to decay to a mass of 1 mg?

10. How long will a house worth $400 000 now take to be worth one million dollars if houses go up 5% per year compounded annually?

Solutions to practice exercises

CHAPTER 1

a) $(x-1)(y+2)$

b) $(a-3b)(d-b+c)$

c) $(x+14)(x-2)$

d) $(x-6)(x-8)$

e) $2x(x-2)(x+8)$

f) $(x-4)(x+1)(x-5)(x+2)$

g) $(10x+9)^2$

h) $3x^3y(x-7)^2$

i) $(2x+3)(x-5)$

j) $(8x-1)(3x+2)$

k) $4x^5(3x+5)(3x-5)$

l) $(x+3y)(x-3y)(x+2y)(x-2y)$

m) $(x-5+y)(x-5-y)$

n) $(5y+3x-2)(5y-3x+2)$

o) $(x-6)(x^2+6x+36)$

p) $4(3x+5)(9x^2-15x+25)$

q) $(x^2+y^2)(x^4-x^2y^2+y^4)$

r) $-2(27x^2+1)$

CHAPTER 2

1. a) $x^2-9x+12$ remainder -10

   b) $3x^3-10x^2+40x-200$ remainder 1006

   c) $4x^2-2x-12$ remainder zero

2. $(x+1)(x-4)$

CHAPTER 3

1. a) -341 b) 0 2. -5

CHAPTER 4

1. a) $(x+2)(x-5)(x-3)$ b) $(x+2)(x-3)(2x-1)$

2. 15

CHAPTER 5

a) $y = (x-9)^2 - 60$

b) $y = 3(x-3)^2 + 22$

c) $y = 2\left(x - \dfrac{5}{4}\right)^2 + \dfrac{23}{8}$

d) $y = \dfrac{3}{4}\left(x - \dfrac{8}{3}\right)^2 + \dfrac{8}{3}$

CHAPTER 6

1. a) $x = \dfrac{3}{2}$ or $x = \dfrac{1}{2}$ (two distinct real roots)

   b) $x = \dfrac{-3}{5}$ (two real and equal roots)

   c) $x = \dfrac{1 \pm \sqrt{-7}}{4}$ (no real roots)

2. 4 and 15   3. 8 and 15   4. 3cm   5. 108 km/h

CHAPTER 7

1. both are 26   2. 15 m x 30m   3. $3.75

CHAPTER 8

a) −3.5 or 4.5   b) $\dfrac{4}{3}$ c) −1

CHAPTER 9

1. a) $x > 7$ or $x < 1$ b) $-1 < x < \dfrac{1}{5}$ c) $x < \dfrac{2}{3}$

CHAPTER 10

1. a) 11   b) 9   c) $\dfrac{17}{8}$

CHAPTER 11

a) $-4 < x < \dfrac{2}{3}$ b) $-3 < x \leq 2$ c) $x < -2$ or $1 \leq x \leq 2$

CHAPTER 12

1. $\dfrac{c^{23} d^{15}}{3}$ 2. a) $a^{10x} b^{7y+14}$ b) 5^{4x+5} 3. x^7

CHAPTER 13

1. a) 1   b) 4   2. $\dfrac{y^3}{2x^7}$

CHAPTER 14

a) 0.04   b) $\dfrac{1}{3}$ c) $\dfrac{625}{81}$ d) 57

CHAPTER 15

a) 6   b) 3   c) 0 or 2   d) $x = -2, y = 4$

CHAPTER 16

1. The domain is all the real numbers and the range is $y > 0$ for all of them. They all pass through (0,1) because of the zero exponent. They are all decreasing functions. The fall of the graph is more rapid as the base increases.
2. The domain is all the real numbers and the range is $y > 0$. The y-intercept is always equal to one. This function is increasing. The rise of the graph is more rapid as the base increases.
3. The domain is all the real numbers and the range is $y > 0$. The y-intercept is always equal to one. The function is decreasing. The fall of the graph is more rapid as the base increases.

CHAPTER 17

1. 2.2 hours   2. 27.4 years   3. 4.75 years

CHAPTER 18

1. a) −4   b) $\dfrac{-3}{2}$ c) $\dfrac{2}{3}$

2. a) 16   b) $\dfrac{1}{4}$

CHAPTER 19

1. a) 2   b) 1

2. 4.98   3. $\log_3 \dfrac{x^{\frac{2}{3}}}{y^{\frac{1}{2}} z^{\frac{5}{2}}}$

CHAPTER 20

a) 100 or 1000   b) 4   c) $\dfrac{1}{8}$ or 8   d) $\dfrac{1}{16}$ or 64

e) 2 or 16   f) 10^{10}

CHAPTER 21

1. 11 months   2. 2292.4 years   3. 31.7 minutes   4. 10.1 years
5. magnitude six 6. 501.2 times as strong   7. 10 000

8. $\left(\dfrac{1}{24}\right)$ th as bright

Solutions to sample exam in algebra

SOLUTIONS TO SAMPLE EXAM IN ALGEBRA

1. a) $x(x-2y) - 3(x-2y) = (x-2y)(x-3)$

   b) $2\left(x^2 + 3x - 18\right) = 2(x-3)(x+6)$

   c) $\left(x^2 - 25y^2\right)\left(x^2 - 9y^2\right) = (x+5y)(x-5y)(x+3y)(x-3y)$

   d) $\left(8x - 3\right)^2$

   e) $x\left(16x^2 - 26x + 9\right) = x(2x-1)(8x-9)$

   f) $x^2 - \left(25y^2 - 20y + 4\right) = x^2 - \left(5y-2\right)^2$

   $$= [x + (5y-2)][x - (5y-2)]$$
   $$= (x+5y-2)(x-5y+2)$$

   g) $\left(8 + \dfrac{3x}{2}\right)\left(8 - \dfrac{3x}{2}\right)$

   h) $\left(\dfrac{x}{2} - 1\right)\left(\dfrac{x^2}{4} + \dfrac{x}{2} + 1\right)$

   i) $(7x + 2y)\left(49x^2 - 14xy + 4y^2\right)$

   j) Since $P(-1) = 0$, by the factor theorem $(x+1)$ is a factor. By long division

   $$\left(x^3 - 5x^2 + 2x + 8\right) \div (x+1) = x^2 - 6x + 8$$

   Therefore we have $(x+1)\left(x^2 - 6x + 8\right)$

   $$= (x+1)(x-2)(x-4).$$

2.

$$3x+2 \overline{\smash{\big)}\ 3x^3 - 4x^2 - 13x - 1} \quad \genfrac{}{}{0pt}{}{x^2 - 2x - 3}{}$$

$$\underline{3x^2 + 2x^2}$$
$$-6x^2 - 13x$$
$$\underline{-6x^2 - 4x}$$
$$-9x - 1$$
$$\underline{-9x - 6}$$
$$5$$

3. $P(-1) = 0, \therefore 5(-1)^3 + k(-1)^2 + 7(-1) - 2 = 0$

i.e. $-5 + k - 7 - 2 = 0,$ therefore $k = 14$.

4. a) By the quadratic formula, $x = \dfrac{3 \pm 13}{16}$, therefore $x = 1$

   or $x = \dfrac{-5}{8}$

   b) $x^2 + 2x + 6 = 0 \therefore x = \dfrac{-2 \pm \sqrt{-20}}{2} = -1 \pm \sqrt{-5}$

   c) By the factor theorem a zero of the left side of the

   equation must be a factor of $\dfrac{4}{6}$. $P(-\dfrac{1}{3}) = 0,$ therefore

   $(x + \dfrac{1}{3})$ or $(3x + 1)$ is a factor.

   $\therefore (3x + 1)(2x^2 - 9x + 4) = (3x + 1)(2x - 1)(x - 4) = 0.$

   Therefore $x = \dfrac{-1}{3}, \dfrac{1}{2}$ and 4.

d)

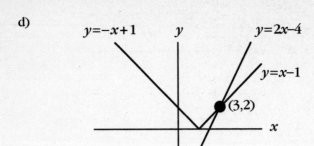

From the diagram, $x = 3$.

e)

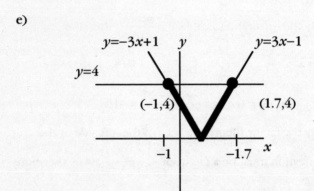

From the diagram, $-1 < x < 1.7$.

f)

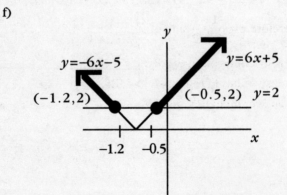

From the diagram, $x \leq -1.2$ or $x \geq -0.5$.

104

g)

	I	II	III
		-1	3
$x+1$	$-$	$+$	$+$
$x-3$	$-$	$-$	$+$
$(x-3)(x+1)$	$+$	$-$	$+$

We have $(x-3)(x+1)>0$.
From the chart we see that regions I and III
satisfy the inequality. Therefore the answer
is $x<-1$ or $x>3$.

h)

	I	II	III	IIII
		-5	-1	3
$x+5$	$-$	$+$	$+$	$+$
$x+1$	$-$	$-$	$+$	$+$
$x-3$	$-$	$-$	$-$	$+$
$\dfrac{-(x+1)}{(x-3)(x+5)}$	$+$	$-$	$+$	$-$

$$\frac{2}{x-3}-\frac{3}{x+5}\le 0 \qquad \therefore \frac{-(x+1)}{(x-3)(x+5)}\le 0$$

The restrictions on the variable are $x \ne -5$ or 3.

The answer lies in regions II and IIII.

The answer including restrictions is $-5<x\le -1$ or $x>3$.

i) $\sqrt{2x+3} = \sqrt{5x+1} - 1$

$\therefore \quad (\sqrt{2x+3})^2 = (\sqrt{5x+1} - 1)^2$

$\therefore \quad 2x+3 = 5x+1 - 2\sqrt{5x+1} + 1$

$\therefore \quad 2\sqrt{5x+1} = 3x - 1$

$\therefore \quad 4(5x+1) = 9x^2 - 6x + 1$

$\therefore \quad 9x^2 - 26x - 3 = 0.$

By the quadratic formula $x = \dfrac{26 \pm 28}{18}$, therefore

$x = \dfrac{-1}{9}$ which does not check or $x = 3$ which does.

5. $\dfrac{y}{3} = x^2 - 6x + \dfrac{25}{3}$

$\therefore \quad \dfrac{y}{3} = (x^2 - 6x + 9) - 9 + \dfrac{25}{3}$

$\therefore \quad \dfrac{y}{3} = (x-3)^2 - 9 + \dfrac{25}{3}$

$\therefore \quad y = 3(x-3)^2 - 27 + 25$ and so $y = 3(x-3)^2 - 2$

6. $y = 600 - 3x,\ A = xy = x(600 - 3x).$

$\therefore \quad A = -3x^2 + 600x.$ To maximize the area,

$x = \dfrac{-b}{2a} = \dfrac{-(600)}{2(-3)} = 100.$

The dimensions should be 100 m by 300 m.

7.

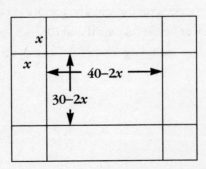

From the diagram, $(40 - 2x)(30 - 2x) = \frac{1}{2}(30)(40)$.

$\therefore \quad 4x^2 - 140x + 600 = 0$.

$\therefore \quad 2x^2 - 70x + 300 = 0$.

$\therefore \quad x^2 - 35x + 150 = 0$.

By **quadratic formula** $x = \frac{35 \pm 25}{2}$.

$x = 30$ or $x = 5$.

The first answer is physically impossible, therefore the width of the frame is 5 cm.

8.

	distance, d	speed, s	time, t
slow way	400	x	$\frac{400}{x}$
fast way	400	$x+5$	$\frac{400}{x+5}$

$\frac{400}{x} - \frac{400}{x+5} = 4$.

$\therefore \quad x(x+5)\left(\frac{400}{x}\right) - x(x+5)\left(\frac{400}{x+5}\right) = 4x(x+5)$.

$\therefore \quad 4x^2 + 20x - 200 = 0$.

$\therefore \quad x^2 + 5x - 500 = 0$. By **quadratic formula** $x = \frac{-5 \pm 45}{2}$.

This gives $x = 20$ as the only physically possible answer. The slower speed is 20 km/h.

Solutions to sample exam on exponents and logarithms

SOLUTIONS TO SAMPLE EXAM ON
EXPONENTS AND LOGARITHMS

1. $\dfrac{\left(16x^{-8}y^{12}\right)\left(27x^{15}y^{-24}\right)}{\left(36x^{-6}y^4\right)(1)} = \dfrac{12x^{13}}{y^{16}}$

2. a) $\left(\dfrac{1}{4}+\dfrac{1}{2}\right)^{-1} = \left(\dfrac{3}{4}\right)^{-1} = \dfrac{4}{3}$ b) $\left(\dfrac{16}{49}\right)^{\frac{3}{2}} = \left(\dfrac{4}{7}\right)^3 = \dfrac{64}{343}$

   c) $\left(27^{\frac{2}{3}}\right)^2 - \left(5^{\frac{1}{2}}\right)^2 = 27^{\frac{4}{3}} - 5 = 76$

3. $\dfrac{3^{3x+15}3^{2-x}}{3^{8x-12}} = 3^{29-6x}$

4. a) $6^{3x-12} = 216, \therefore 6^{3x-12} = 6^3 \therefore 3x-12 = 3$ and so $x = 5$.
   b) $5^x + 5^2 5^x = 16250, \therefore (1+25)5^x = 16250,$
      $\therefore 26 \cdot 5^x = 16250, \therefore 5^x = 625, \therefore 5^x = 5^4$ and so $x = 4$.
   c) $2^{2x+y} = 2^4, \therefore 2x + y = 4.$ Also $(2^3)^x = (2^2)^{y+3},$
      $\therefore 2^{3x} = 2^{2y+6}, \therefore 3x = 2y + 6.$
      Solving the two equations in two unknowns gives
      $x = 2$ and $y = 0.$

5. a) $\dfrac{3}{2}$

   b) $\log_3 (27)^{-1} = -\log_3 (3^3) = -3\log_3 3 = (-3)(1) = -3$

   c) $\log_{25} 5^3 = 3\log_{25} 5 = (3)(\dfrac{1}{2}) = \dfrac{3}{2}$

   d) $(9^2)^{\log_9 5} = 9^{2\log_9 5} = 9^{\log_9 5^2} = 5^2 = 25$

6. a) $\log_x 7^3 = 3, \ \therefore 3\log_x 7 = 3, \ \therefore \log_x 7 = 1$ and hence $x = 7$.

   b) $x = 8^{\frac{2}{3}}$ and hence $x = 4$.

   c) $\log_6 (x+3)(x-2) = 1,$
      $\therefore \log_6 (x^2 + x - 6) = 1, \ \therefore x^2 + x - 6 = 6$
      $\therefore x^2 + x - 12 = 0, \ \therefore (x+4)(x-3) = 0, \ x = -4$ is rejected,
      $\therefore$ the only solution is $x = 3$.

   d) Let $y = \log x, \ \therefore y^2 + y - 6 = 0, \therefore (y+3)(y-2) = 0,$
      $\therefore y = -3 \ or \ y = 2. \ \therefore \ \log x = -3 \ $ or $ \ \log x = 2,$
      $\therefore x = 10^{-3} = \dfrac{1}{1000} \ or \ x = 10^2 = 100.$

   e) $\log[x^{\log x}] = \log 10\ 000. \ \therefore (\log x)(\log x) = 4, \ \therefore \log^2 x = 4,$
      $\therefore \log x = 2, \ \therefore x = 100, \ $ or $\log x = -2$ which gives $x = \dfrac{1}{100}.$

7. $\log \left(a^2 \right)^{\frac{2}{3}} + 5\log \left(b^{\frac{1}{2}} \right) + \log c^{-1}$

   $= \log a^{\frac{4}{3}} + \log b^{\frac{5}{2}} - \log c = \log a^{\frac{4}{3}} b^{\frac{5}{2}} - \log c = \log \dfrac{a^{\frac{4}{3}} b^{\frac{5}{2}}}{c}$

8. a) $N(t) = c \cdot 2^{\frac{t}{d}}$ where $c = 7500, t = 1$ and $N(1) = 20000,$
      $\therefore \ 20000 = 7500 \cdot 2^{\frac{1}{d}}, \ \therefore 2^{\frac{1}{d}} = \dfrac{8}{3}, \ \therefore \log 2^{\frac{1}{d}} = \log \dfrac{8}{3},$

      $\therefore \dfrac{1}{d} \log 2 = \log \dfrac{8}{3}, \ \therefore \dfrac{\log 2}{d} = \dfrac{\log \dfrac{8}{3}}{1}, \ \therefore d = \dfrac{\log 2}{\log \dfrac{8}{3}} = 0.71$ hour.

b) Since .71 hour = 42.4 minutes ...

For $N(t) = 60\,000$, $60\,000 = 7500 \cdot 2^{\frac{t}{42.4}}$, $\therefore 2^{\frac{t}{42.4}} = 8$,

$\therefore 2^{\frac{t}{42.4}} = 2^3$, $\therefore \dfrac{t}{42.4} = 3$ and so $t = 127.2$ min.

9. $m(t) = c \cdot 2^{\frac{-t}{b}}$ where $c = 60$, $b = 16$, and $N(t) = 1$,

$\therefore \quad 1 = 60 \cdot 2^{\frac{-t}{16}}$, $\therefore \dfrac{1}{60} = 2^{\frac{-t}{16}}$,

$\therefore \quad \log 60^{-1} = \log 2^{\frac{-t}{16}}$, $\therefore -\log 60 = \dfrac{-t}{16} \log 2$,

$\therefore \quad t = 94.5$ days.

10. $A = P(1+i)^n$ where $P = 400\,000$, $i = 0.05$, $A = 1\,000\,000$,

$\therefore \quad 1\,000\,000 = 400\,000(1.05)^n$,

$\therefore \quad (1.05)^n = 2.5$,

$\therefore \quad \log(1.05)^n = \log 2.5$,

$\therefore \quad n \log 1.05 = \log 2.5$,

$\therefore \quad n = \dfrac{\log 2.5}{\log 1.05} = 18.8$ years

**For fifty years, Coles Notes have been helping
students get through high school and university.
New Coles Notes will help get you through the rest of life.**

Look for these NEW COLES NOTES!

GETTING ALONG IN ...

- French
- Spanish
- Italian
- German
- Russian

HOW TO ...

- Write Effective Business Letters
- Write a Great Résumé
- Do A Great Job Interview
- Start Your Own Small Business
- Buy and Sell Your Home
- Plan Your Estate

YOUR GUIDE TO ...

- Basic Investing
- Mutual Funds
- Investing in Stocks
- Speed Reading
- Public Speaking
- Wine
- Effective Business Presentations

MOMS AND DADS' GUIDE TO ...

- Basketball for Kids
- Baseball for Kids
- Soccer for Kids
- Hockey for Kids
- Gymnastics for Kids
- Martial Arts for Kids
- Helping Your Child in Math
- Raising A Reader
- Your Child: The First Year
- Your Child: The Terrific Twos
- Your Child: Age Three and Four

HOW TO GET AN A IN ...

- Sequences & Series
- Trigonometry & Circle Geometry
- Senior Algebra with Logs & Exponents
- Permutations, Combinations & Probability
- Statistics & Data Analysis
- Calculus
- Senior Physics
- Senior English Essays
- School Projects & Presentations

**Coles Notes and New Coles Notes are available at the following
stores: Chapters • Coles • Smithbooks • World's Biggest Bookstore**

NOTES & UPDATES